THE EMPLOYMENT OF NURSES

The Employment of Nurses

NURSING LABOUR TURNOVER IN THE NHS

G. MERCER

CROOM HELM   LONDON

© 1979 Geoffrey Mercer
Croom Helm Ltd., 2-10 St John's Road, SW11

British Library Cataloguing in Publication Data

Mercer, Geoffrey
   The employment of nurses.
   1. Nurses – Great Britain – Supply and demand
   2. Great Britain – National Health Service
   I. Title
   331.7'61'36210425 RT11
   ISBN 0-7099-0015-5

Printed in Great Britain by offset lithography by
Billing & Sons Ltd, Guildford, London and Worcester

CONTENTS

ACKNOWLEDGEMENTS

The origins of this book lie in a project funded by the DHSS in 1975-6 on labour turnover in nursing. I am grateful therefore for the opportunity to record my thanks for the generous assitance provided by the DHSS and the many nurses who co-operated so fully during that study. Needless to say, neither the DHSS, nor individual nurses can be held responsible for the views expressed here.

The study also depended on academic contributions, and the following in particular offered valuable aid and advice: Laura Taggart, Christina Taylor, Sue Kilroe, Roger Appleyard, Malcolm Povey, Bernadette Fallon, Christine Smale, David Dunkerley and Andrew Long. Most important of all, however, was Claire Mould, who not only lasted from the beginning to the end of the investigation, but played a crucial role in its administration and in the writing of the final Report. All that said, I alone must be held to account for what appears here.

1 INTRODUCTION: LABOUR TURNOVER IN NURSING

Background

National Health Service employment in the 1970s has been plagued by a continuing divergence between the demand for, and supply of, nursing staff. 'Hospitals face crisis over nurse shortage,' proclaimed a newspaper headline in mid-1978. 'Lack of recruits, not cash threatens the service.'[1] Yet at that time unemployment figures included several thousand nurses, and would have been much higher if all those women willing to return to nursing when a suitable vacancy arose had registered officially. Talk of a shortfall in nurses seems even more absurd when one recalls the fears expressed less than two years previously that the National Health Service (NHS) was producing trained staff who were surplus to requirements. In reaction, the recruitment of student and pupil nurses was cut back, those finishing their training were warned that they could not be guaranteed employment, and older staff were persuaded — often very unwillingly — into early retirement or 'prophylactic redundancy'.[2] These about-turns, and within such a short time period, signify a waste of scarce human and financial resources, and provoke scepticism about the efficiency of personnel forecasting in the service. While this aspect of nurse management has gained increasing credence and formal recognition, especially since the reorganisation of the Health Service in 1974, it has yet to demonstrate its efficacy in a practical, comprehensive programme for action.[3] Indeed, the General Secretary of the Royal College of Nurses (RCN) declared recently that 'The urgent need is for manpower planning policies, which the D.H.S.S. [Department of Health and Social Security] just does not have for nurses.'[4] In this book, I shall examine a key element in any such plan for nurse employment, namely the level and character of labour turnover.

Labour turnover, as an object of industrial and academic concern, gained prominence in the first quarter of this century, and although interest has fluctuated since then, it has attracted considerable attention over the past two decades.[5] Throughout this period labour turnover has been acknowledged as an unacceptable feature of employment practice, and hence its widespread designation as a 'bad thing'. In their seminal contribution, Brissenden and Frankel expressed over fifty years ago the opinion that

> Labour instability is regarded by all those who have given any
> serious consideration to the problem as one of the maladjustments
> of our industrial life, wasteful and destructive of the potential
> manpower of the nation and a serious obstacle to the complete
> utilization of the country's productive resources.[6]

Appraised from this perspective, high labour turnover, or the
underlying malaise which it implies, has acted as an important spur
to a wide range of organisational innovations. These stretch from
'scientific management', through schemes for improved 'human
relations' and 'job enrichment', to more fundamental plans to
transform the labour process and the social relations at work. Each
of these has been advanced as an antidote to that employee behaviour,
of which high labour turnover is but one part, deemed to have
deleterious consequences for organisational efficiency and well-being.[7]

~ The objective of this book is to examine the nature of this general
unease with labour turnover in the specific instance of trained nurses
in British hospitals. Unfortunately, accurate commentary on the level
and character of such turnover, and not only in nursing, is hampered
by the paucity of reliable information. Nevertheless, official
confirmation that the NHS has experienced many difficulties in the
retention, and (though less so) in the recruitment of its nursing
work-force is contained in the Briggs *Report on Nursing*, which
presented a full account of the situation in the late 1960s and the
early 1970s.[8] This recommended that the formulation of policies in
this area should be given priority. But the information then available
was not sufficient to generate the sophisticated analysis on which any
manpower action plan would have to be based. Nor was there
anything in the pipeline. This lack of knowledge extended over every
aspect of the internal labour market in nursing. Some national
turnover rates had been calculated,[9] but little was known about the
variation between different grades of nurse, between types of hospital,
and so forth. Furthermore, there was 'little information on movement
between different areas of the National Health Service and into and
out of the N.H.S.'[10] Hence one of Briggs's central recommendations
that more detailed investigations be carried out on the level and pattern
of stability and mobility among nurses. This would also necessitate
more detailed statistics on the supply and demand for staff in nursing
as set against the wider or external labour market.

That plea was the seed from which this study grew. But as we shall explain in more detail later, the intention was to extend the survey of nursing turnover beyond the calculation of mobility rates, that is, over and above the disembodied manifestation of this form of human behaviour, to explore what is, after all, 'inter-human actions in terms of the meanings they have to the parties involved as well as in terms of specific physical changes'.[11] Our approach has been to place nursing turnover against a backcloth of work and non-work conditions, rather than as a phenomenon artificially isolated from its extended social setting. Labour turnover is treated as a social process. In this investigation the subjective meanings held by those nurses who formed the basis of the project will figure as prominently in the discussion which follows as the structural constraints of their social situation. Too much turnover research has dismissed these factors as irrelevant or at most incidental. In consequence, the focus of this study is not primarily on labour turnover as a problem of 'organisational decay', but as a considered form of social action, in an employment situation where a certain amount of labour mobility is normal and beneficial, both for individual nurses and for the NHS as their employer.

Studying Turnover

A concern about recruiting, and retaining, an adequate number of suitable nurses is hardly novel, and can be seen in the pronouncements of interested persons at least as far back as Florence Nightingale — who is generally credited with a pivotal role in the development of modern nursing.[12] The subject has, however, gathered momentum as a matter for professional debate, particularly with the creation of the National Health Service. Notwithstanding this, disquiet about the quality and quantity of their employees unites both public and private employers and in practice many of those factors which have led to what is regarded as an unacceptable level of turnover in nursing are also present in other occupational sectors. While the predicament faced by the nursing authorities has many specific features, they are far from being confronted by problems which are unique to NHS nursing. In our opinion the contemporary concern over nursing turnover springs from three main sources. They are: (1) the changing economic, and obviously employment, situation, together with the level of state expenditure which is regarded as reasonable for a public service; (2) the growth of a philosophy of corporate management in nursing, associated with an increasing bureaucratisation of the Health Service; and (3) the changing role of women in contemporary society, and the specific part played by women in paid employment, which has obvious ramifications for a predominantly female work-force as there is in nursing. Taken together, these constitute the key parameters which have conditioned this research into nursing turnover, and will therefore be spelt out in rather greater detail.

Economic Climate

The impact on labour turnover of economic conditions takes two forms. The first, and more direct relationship stems from the well established, negative correlation between the level of unemployment and the rate of turnover. With high unemployment and a low level of job vacancies, employees will be less inclined, and less able, to search for alternative employment. Equally, they will be less likely to give up work to take a break, since their prospects of a speedy return when they are ready will be bleak. As a rule, the majority of those who change jobs of their own accord do so after they have been accepted in a new post. Furthermore, one presumes that that small minority who are willing to take a chance and hand in their notice before they have obtained other work will not only be small, but will actually diminish relative to the more circumspect majority in these unfavourable economic conditions. Employers too may react to what is for them a more comfortable situation by taking steps to improve the quality of their work-force. They can, for example, be more discriminating in their selection of new staff, and can eschew those whom they believe to constitute a poor employment risk. But while research has invariably demonstrated a strong connection between economic conditions and the rate of turnover in the country as a whole, it has also been noted that there are marked variations, for example, between industries, between different occupational groups in the same industry, and between different parts of the country.[13] To take one illustration that has attracted much attention, the existence of a 'local labour market' can exert a significant impression on both the supply of, and demand for, nursing labour.[14]

In the world of nursing there have, over the years, been repeated references to the difficulty that the NHS has had in retaining its staff, and of the real shortages in some areas. This has been aligned to an atmosphere where nurses have become accustomed to the opportunities for frequent changes of job, or taking breaks from work, secure in the knowledge that they would not have too much trouble in obtaining nursing employment again when they were ready to return — although perhaps some geographical mobility might be necessary, or the hours

offered might not be wholly acceptable.[15] In large part, nursing has
been able to tolerate this level of mobility because of the large pool of
trained staff wanting to return to work, and because there was an
adequate flow of young recruits into training schools. With respect to
women, alternative employment possibilities have been in short supply,
but in the professions, nursing, along with school-teaching, have long
been exceptions.[16] In the last few years, however, even these groups
have experienced fluctuating fortunes on the labour market. Thus
qualified nursing staff have endured difficulties in finding suitable work,
and for nurses as a whole the number registered as unemployed
increased by a staggering 83 per cent between June and December
1975.[17] According to most reports, the level of job-changing hitherto
characteristic of nursing has slumped in reaction to these trends in the
economy. With Health Service employment chances generally depressed,
any thoughts that married women might have had of giving up their
work — perhaps only on a temporary basis — or of moving elsewhere
are greatly diminished. In a period of inflation and unemployment the
husband's job outlook will also be clouded, and when two wages have
become a necessity for so many households to achieve what they
consider to be a decent standard of life, women will be even less
inclined to leave their current employment.

The less direct influence of changing economic conditions on labour
turnover stems from the considerable difficulties that have confronted
the state in its efforts to manage the economy generally, and the
specific pressures on it to reduce state expenditure. Inflation and
unemployment have both risen sharply and 'unproductive' state
expenditure has borne much of the blame.[18] The NHS, as one of the
largest recipients of state expenditure, has been an obvious target for
cuts. The attack on the public sector has also entailed demands that it
become more efficient — or cost-effective — in the management of its
resources. This has stimulated the development of manpower planning
in the Health Service, and particularly significant for this study, it has
encouraged efforts to reduce the level of labour turnover by the
imposition of tighter managerial control.

Growth of Managerialism

Quite evidently it is not only in the NHS that difficulties in ensuring
adequate control of the organisation led to the search for new styles of
management, but the public sector represented in the 1960s a
particularly fertile ground. The shift was towards corporate
management, which was identified with a total view of the organisation,

and *inter alia* advocated distinct lines of responsibility.[19] Examination
of recent alterations of the structure of nursing demonstrates how such
'managerialism' has overthrown traditional forms of administration.
The most obvious landmark in this process is the Salmon Report which
appeared in 1966, but the new management structure which it
encouraged was greatly bolstered by the reorganisation of the National
Health Service in 1974. In consequence, a revamped career structure
was instituted, and this included a level of nurse administrators who
were expected to adopt a 'pure management' orientation.[20] It is not
difficult to understand why nursing should become an early quarry for
those intent on annexing the modern, rational techniques of business
management. Within the NHS budget, labour costs amount to
approximately three-quarters of total expenditure, and nurses
constitute the largest group of NHS employees, at almost 45 per cent
of all staff.[21] The pursuit of greater efficiency and worker productivity
therefore quickly became an acceptable part of the nurse manager's job.
    The new breed of manager was taught to treat labour instability as a
malfunction within the organisation, and to take appropriate remedial
action. A low level of labour movement was one goal, on the assumption
that labour productivity and efficiency increased the longer a person
stayed in their post; while in addition, the cost of replacing old staff
and recruiting and then training their replacements was considered
wasteful, both in terms of people's time and the organisation's budget.
To most people, the task for nurse managers seems daunting. There
are obvious pitfalls in any attempt to determine the productivity of
service occupations such as nursing. The nurse motto — tender, loving
care (TLC) — runs counter to cost evaluation or cost-benefit procedures.
Nevertheless, the search for criteria to assess nursing output has
received weighty official backing. For example, the Briggs Report
argued forcefully that it was imperative to 'develop measurements of
the "output" of nursing and midwifery services', and later expressed
the view that it ought to be possible both 'to speak of the objectives
of a particular unit or sector of the services in terms of "target levels"
of their outputs [and] . . .to compare over time measurements of output
of different units or sectors of their sub-divisions'.[22] Even if the direct
estimation of nursing productivity has not progressed very far,
mechanisms have been devised to increase the length of service record
of those nurses who are deemed especially necessary for the
maintenance of a health service.
    Such practices have been highlighted elsewhere in studies which have
identified something akin to a 'dual labour market', and this concept

displays some close parallels with the position in nursing.[23] Barron and Norris categorise a dual labour market as one in which:

(1) There is a more or less pronounced division into higher paying and lower paying sectors; (2) mobility across the boundary of these sectors is restricted; (3) higher paying jobs are tied into promotional or career ladders, while lower paid jobs offer few opportunities for vertical movement; (4) higher paying jobs are relatively stable, while lower paid jobs are unstable.[24]

The dividing line then separates a primary sector of better paid and more stable jobs, from a secondary sector where pay is worse and the conditions of work less secure, and less attractive generally. While it is accepted that the schism will vary across labour markets, it does not seem unreasonable to identify distinct job clusters in nursing. To start with, there is the veritable chasm between the trained and the untrained nursing staff — indeed most of the former deny that the latter are really nurses at all. But even within the trained ranks there is a gulf. For example, registered staff, who alone among nurses have the opportunity to rise to the top of their profession, have been charged with offloading some of their less attractive and routine work to others, usually one of their untrained or junior colleagues, such as nursing auxiliaries or trainees, although the often delicate apportionment of tasks between registered and enrolled staff has been a considerable bone of contention. It may also work the other way, so that a form of de-skilling takes place across all trained nursing staff so that more and more are ranked in a secondary segment. However, at the present time registered staff in general still rate as a relatively privileged group, and the dividing line between them and other nurses is maintained by incentives and measures to instil an elite consciousness and thereby encourage their retention in the labour force. The usual inducements are financial, although in some instances status rewards are substituted. Indeed in nursing something close to 'hierarchy fetishism' has long been practised, and the objective of stability in selected groups of staff is pursued without apparent recourse to monetary rewards. The end result is supposed to be that mobility in the primary sector is basically upward as befits a hierarchically organised career structure, while movement in the secondary market is essentially horizontal between industries and occupations. In the specific instance of female employees there may be a relatively far greater readiness to move between the unskilled and semiskilled sectors compared with male workers.[25] For management, however, the goal is to stabilise the more highly qualified nursing staff, and to ensure that they carry out those tasks which they were 'really trained to do'.

This also entails an extensive training programme for management itself. Increasingly nursing, like other areas, has become the object of all manner of initiatives inspired by the work of industrial psychologists in particular to improve both the quality of work as well as to bring it under more effective control and to standardise it. Managerial innovation and influence in nursing — as it has affected both those inside and outside the clinical situation — thus displays many similarities to the reform of work relations carried out in private industry.[26] Again the control of labour turnover has been a recurring theme. But if optimism has been frequently expressed, concrete achievements have been thin on the ground. Despite this, the conviction inspired in each new nurse manager's breast is that their intervention will win out in the end.

Women in Work

To a degree then, greater occupational distinctiveness and the level of labour turnover interact with one another. Nevertheless, as several have pointed out,

> it is very easy to confuse properties of jobs with characteristics of job holders, because individuals who are confined to a particular sector of the labour market will acquire histories and attitudes which reflect their jobs and which mark them off from workers who do not share the same experiences.[27]

This comment has obvious relevance for a study of a predominantly female work-force as in nursing, where the frequently mentioned higher turnover rate may be a function of the jobs held rather than their qualities as women. 'A failure to unravel the different strands of "individual" and "structural" causation can lead to a crude reification of individual characteristics and an unwarranted emphasis upon those characteristics as causes.'[28] In practice, the criteria advanced as likely to identify secondary workers by Barron and Norris do not differ greatly from the popular stereotype of women workers. As Beechey notes, their approach also suffers from a lack of concrete analysis of the work process, and specifically ignores the resistance by workers to an employer's attempts to develop a strategy along dual market lines.[29]

However, this argument may itself underestimate the efforts of some employee organisations in nursing to accelerate a primary market location for their members. What is therefore required is a wider analysis of the changing demand for female labour — one which recognises the significance of the 'sexual division of labour' in any labour market strategy. In addition due recognition must be given to the position of nurses as state employees.[30]

Although nursing has been an overwhelmingly female occupation, at least over the past hundred years, it is only in recent decades that there has been a general expansion of wage labour among women. For example, in 1931 only 10 per cent of married women were in employment, while in 1951 the number had risen to 21.7 per cent, and then doubled again to 42.2 per cent by 1971.[31] The growth of work participation rates has been most visible among married women, largely because of the dramatic increase in vacancies for part-time work during the last twenty years, and few areas demonstrate this trend as much as the public sector. In nursing, according to the DHSS returns for March 1975, of the 338,171 nurses of all grades in hospital posts in England and Wales, slightly over 90 per cent were women. Within the female ranks, some 45 per cent were part-timers, which represents an increase of approximately 15 per cent over the previous 15 years. This predominance of women in nursing, and their almost total presence in the part-time category, must mean that any study of nurses cannot but be an examination of women in the labour process. This raises specific problems, since women, to an extent not true of men, are caught in a dilemma where they are expected to adhere to the demands not only of their work, but also their family role — as wife and mother.[32] This is not to deny the contribution of male nurses — indeed their over-representation in the higher administrative grades is well established[33] — but simply recognition that the form of pressure upon women in general will most probably be present within a nursing population. Exactly how the role and condition of women in contemporary society are mediated and expressed through work as a nurse is therefore of central concern in this investigation. While female nurses are directly engaged in wage labour, in addition to their contribution to domestic labour, they fall prey to a dual consciousness, or the 'feminine dilemma'. The stereotype reaction to women at work has been, if not outright condemnation, at least an insistence that outside work should not be allowed to interfere with her central duties as wife and mother.[34] Hence the husband's job and interests are traditionally accorded priority. What is more, women with family responsibilities usually face severe practical difficulties in ensuring that, for example, children are looked after while mother is at work. The state has not seen fit to act in this area, and it is therefore left to individual employers whether they will accept responsibility, or take initiatives to facilitate the employment of women. Within the NHS there is some evidence that the authorities have been rather less unsympathetic than most employers in the provision of nursery/creche places, but the vast majority do not obtain proper cover.[35] Again, women's work role is downgraded by the widespread expectation that her career will play second fiddle to that of her husband. This can mean that it is the nature of the husband's job, as much as the marital bond, which inhibits a woman from working. Thus the spouse of a person employed in a post characterised by frequent geographical mobility (such as bank employees) will find it most difficult to develop their own career.

It is in these circumstances that the argument has increasingly been voiced that there exists a 'sexual division of labour'.[36] Thus while women have entered employment in increasing numbers, they have typically been drawn into the poorly paid, public-sector, service jobs, many of which still carry strong overtones of their 'other role' as housewife and mother. In this respect, nursing is a paradigm case, since the good nurse is still very much expected to display motherly and other feminine attributes. The sexual division of labour describes a subordinate position at both home and work for women. It is evident that they are severely under-represented in positions of power and authority; and this is true even of nursing. Some have actually attempted to interpret the growth of managerialism in nursing as part of a sexist gambit which downgrades the traditional method of administration (associated particularly with Matron, and 'feminine' procedures), and replaces it with modern management techniques (essentially bureaucratic and 'male-dominated' procedures).[37]

A further aspect of this sexual division of labour stems from the way in which women are regarded as the more flexible element in the employment market — that may be expanded or reduced in size as economic prospects determine. The suggestion has been that official policy has encouraged a division in the labour force between a group of more qualified personnel who are intended for long-term careers in the service, and those others — whether untrained, part-time or enrolled — whose future is less rosy, and whose stability is not as sought after. In practice, the existence of an ample reserve of nurses rather diminishes the worries of management about labour instability since recruitment has rarely been a problem. However, the diminution of any such pool of unemployed nurses constitutes a threat to organisational efficiency since even a 'normal' level of labour mobility is difficult to counter. When the economy goes into decline, it is the untrained, part-time female worker who bears the burden. This is made even more pertinent by the comments expressed in influential circles about the need to increase the proportion of part-time nurses in the NHS.[38] The Briggs Report, for example, emphasised that it is cheaper, in terms of both money and management time, to bring back former nurses into work rather than to recruit and train new staff. Utilisation of the part-timers pool is also encouraged by suggestions that their rate of absenteeism and general instability is less, and their productivity actually higher, than that of their full-time colleagues.[39] According to several surveys, as many as one half of all married nurses return to their profession after a break, although this still allows scope for further exploitation of these trained resources. None the less, there is an obvious inference that many women see their absence from work as no more than a temporary interlude. In consequence, a relatively higher level of female instability in nursing might be accepted without undue alarm because the majority will be intent on returning to the NHS at some later date. The temporary character of their absence might even be less troublesome for nursing management than male turnover, which if not as acute, entailed relatively more frequently a complete loss of staff from the NHS. In this respect, the behaviour of women contrasts markedly with that of their male colleagues. Of course, those factors which impress themselves on job stability demonstrate similarities, irrespective of whether the worker is male or female, young or old, black or white. And yet due allowance must be accorded to the social conditions of those who do move between jobs. In the case of women, our argument is that there will be particular pressures that flow from the sexual division of labour as set against a dual labour market strategy.

Summary

In this brief introduction an attempt has been made to situate labour turnover within the context not only of nursing but of the wider forces which impinge upon those in employment (or unemployment). The factors mentioned are by no means an exhaustive list, but it is contended that the complex interaction of structural changes in employment patterns, within the NHS in particular and in advanced capitalism in general, and the extension of corporate management ideas and techniques into the Health Service, when set against the wider backcloth of economic decline and crisis in Britain, have combined to orchestrate both the level and pattern of labour turnover in nursing. This applies to the degree to which such mobility is deemed to be a significant problem, as well as to the type of corrective measures which are formulated to bring it under control.

Before we outline what emerge in this study as the essential features of nursing turnover, we shall explore in more detail the background to turnover *per se* — what it comprises, and how it is measured.

Notes

1. *Guardian*, 8 May 1978.

2. M. Gray, 'Angels with no Muscle', *Health and Social Service Journal*, 29 October 1976, p.1934.

3. The most notable changes in the career structure of nursing in recent years followed the publication of the Salmon Report in 1966.

4. *Guardian*, 23 February 1977.

5. For a record of the changing profile of publications on labour turnover, see B.O. Pettman (ed.), *Labour Turnover and Retention* (Gower Press, London, 1973), p.xiv.

6. P.F. Brissenden and E. Frankel, *Labour Turnover in Industry: a Statistical Analysis* (Macmillan, New York, 1922), p.1.

7. See K. Hawkins, *Conflict and Change* (Holt, Rinehart and Winston, London, 1972); P.D. Anthony, *The Ideology of Work* (Tavistock, London 1977); D. Silverman, *The Theory of Organisations* (Heinemann, London 1970).

8. A. Briggs (Chairman), *Report of the Committee on Nursing* (HMSO, London, 1972), Cmnd. 7115.

9. Ibid., pp.122-4.

10. Ibid., p.236.

11. D. Martindale, *The Nature and Types of Sociological Theory* (Routledge and Kegan Paul, London, 1958), p.51.

12. B. Abel-Smith, *A History of the Nursing Profession* (Heinemann, London 1966); F. Nightingale, *Notes on Nursing: What it is and what it is not*, 1st edn. (Harrison and Sons, London, 1859).

13. J.R. Long, *Labour Turnover under Full Employment*, Studies in Economics and Society, Monograph A2 (University of Birmingham, 1951); H. Behrend, 'Absence and Labour Turnover in a Changing Economic Climate', *Occupational Psychology*, vol.27 (1955), pp. 69-79; H. Behrend, 'A Note on Labour Turnover and the Individual Factory', *Journal of Industrial Economics*, vol.22 (1953), pp.58-64.

14. D.I. Mackay, D. Boddy, J. Brack, J. Diack and N. Jones, *Labour Markets* (Allen and Unwin, London, 1971); Briggs, *Report of the Committee on Nursing*, pp.137-45; E. Nelson, *The Market Place for Manpower*. Report for Southampton and S.W. Hampshire Health District (Southampton, 1977).

15. Briggs, *Report of the Committee on Nursing*, pp.120-1.

16. Department of Employment, *Women and Work: A Statistical Survey*, Manpower Paper no.9 (HMSO, London, 1974); B.N. Seear, *Re-entry of Women to the Labour Market after an Interruption in Employment* (OECD, Paris, 1971).

17. Counter Information Services (CIS), *Cutting the Welfare State*, no 13 (London, n.d.).

18. J. O'Connor, *The Fiscal Crisis of the State* (St Martin's Press, New York,

1973); I. Gough, 'State Expenditure in Advanced Capitalism', *New Left Review*, no.92 (1975), pp.53-92.

19. See R.L. Ackoff, *A Concept of Corporate Planning* (Wiley-Interscience, New York, 1970). For a study of the application of corporate planning in local government more generally, see C. Cockburn, *The Local State* (Pluto Press, London, 1977).

20. For a fuller review of these changes see M. Carpenter, 'The New Managerialism and Professionalism in Nursing' in M. Stacey *et al.* (eds.), *Health and the Division of Labour* (Croom Helm, London, 1977), pp.165-93.

21. T. Manson, 'Management, the Professions and the Unions' in Stacey *et al.*, *Health and the Division of Labour*, pp.196-214.

22. Briggs, *Report of the Committee on Nursing*, p.151.

23. D.M. Gordon, *Theories of Poverty and Underemployment* (D.C. Heath, Lexington, 1972); R.D. Barron and G.M. Norris, 'Sexual Divisions and the Dual Labour Market' in D. Barker and S. Allen (eds.), *Dependence and Exploitation in Work and Marriage* (Longman, London, 1976).

24. Barron and Norris, 'Sexual Divisions and the Dual Labour Market', p.49.

25. V. Beechey, 'Women and Production: a Critical Analysis of Some Sociological Theories of Women's Work' in A Kuhn and A. Wolpe (eds.), *Feminism and Materialism* (Routledge and Kegan Paul, London, 1978).

26. H. Braverman, *Labour and Monopoly Capital* (Monthly Review Press, New York, 1974).

27. Barron and Norris, 'Sexual Divisions and the Dual Labour Market', p.50.

28. Ibid., p.50.

29. Beechey, 'Women and Production', pp.172-81.

30. Ibid., p.179.

31. Department of Employment, *Women and Work: A Review*, Manpower Paper no.11 (HMSO, London, 1975).

32. A. Myrdal and V. Klein, *Women's Two Roles* (Routledge and Kegan Paul, London, 1970); R. Rapoport and N. Rapoport, *Dual Career Families* (Penguin, Harmondsworth, 1971).

33. R.G.S. Brown and R.W. Stones, *The Male Nurse*, Occasional Papers on Social Administration, no.52 (Bell, London, 1973).

34. H. Gavron, *The Captive Wife* (Penguin, Harmondsworth, 1966).

35. G. Mercer and R. Minhas, 'Who Needs a Nursery?', unpublished report, University of Leeds, 1975.

36. J. Gardiner, 'Women's Domestic Labour', *New Left Review* (no.89; 1975-6), pp.47-58; J. Gardiner, 'Women in the Labour Process and Class Structure' in A. Hunt (ed.), *Class and Class Structure* (Lawrence and Wishart, London, 1977).

37. R. Austin, 'Sex and Gender in the Future of Nursing', Parts 1 and 2, *Nursing Times*, 25 August and 1 September 1977.

38. Briggs, *Report of the Committee on Nursing*, chs. IV and V.

39. Department of Employment, *Women and Work: A Review*, pp 51-7.

2 WHAT IS LABOUR TURNOVER? DEFINITION AND MEASUREMENT

If one thing characterises investigations of labour turnover it is that the area under scrutiny is subject to constantly changing boundary lines, has no accepted vocabulary, and hence generates considerable latitude in the interpretation of what the term 'really means'. Comparison between studies is inhibited by this diversity in terminology which sometimes denotes a different area of study or approach, but not always. Turnover, instability, separations, departures, quits, mobility, movement, wastage — this list by no means exhausts the range of labels which have found currency. We have tried to tread what is the often illusory middle ground between the pedants and those other commentators who assume that 'everybody knows' what is meant by turnover and that no elaboration is necessary. Therefore the first step in this chapter is to locate our understanding and use of the term 'labour turnover'.

In our opinion too much of the literature has been overly imbued with the assumption that labour turnover is adequately described when a rate of turnover has been identified. In a barely developed form it leads to a perspective where the mobility of labour — meaning primarily 'leavers' — is translated into one of the following dichotomies: (1) voluntary versus involuntary; or (2) controllable versus uncontrollable turnover. From our standpoint these classifications are unduly restrictive and the decision to stay in, or move from, a particular place of employment should be treated as an instance of meaningful behaviour to those involved. Nursing turnover is regarded as

a form of rational social action — whether or not its rationality is conceived in terms of economic motivation. The decision to leave, and the decision to stay, both represent the workers' response to an objective situation, as it is mediated by its own values, expectations and perceptions'.[1]

This does not mean that the subjective dimension is everything, so that an individual's attitudes independently 'cause' turnover; instead social research should analyse the structural constraints and possibilities of a particular conjuncture, and ally this with a parallel examination of what may admittedly constitute a poorly formed subjective viewpoint.

Definitions of Labour Turnover

Two basic definitions of turnover predominate in the existing literature, although not all studies are explicit about the premises from which they begin.[2] First, and the one most often encountered, is that which equates turnover with termination of employment. This invariably results in an exclusive preoccupation with leavers from an organisation. Against this, there is a second school of thought which adopts a more wide-ranging interpretation. The province of turnover research is then expanded to encompass joining, leaving and staying in an organisation. This formulation has been much influenced by the writings of Brissenden and Frankel.[3] In fact, these authors are more precise in their use of terms than some who claim to be influenced by them. Brissenden and Frankel employ 'labour mobility' as an umbrella phrase; while labour turnover is reserved for a very specific phenomenon incorporating the recruitment of new staff to compensate for leavers. It is identified as 'the extent of shift and replacement necessary for the maintenance of the workforce'.[4] We accept that turnover should not be restricted to movement out of an organisation, since that contradicts the problem as it is experienced within an organisation, and as importantly for our discussion, it rejects any approach based on a full consideration of behaviour and attitudes in work. But we do not agree that turnover is solely a matter of labour replacement. Indeed the orientation of Brissenden and Frankel leads to such unhappy descriptions as that where recruitment has not fully compensated for departures as an instance of nil turnover. As we will argue later, it is obviously important in the calculation of turnover rates, as in manpower planning generally, to know whether or not the size of the work-force is constant, but our view is that confusion will outweigh any benefit by acceptance of the designation of turnover advocated by Brissenden and Frankel. As a consequence, our understanding of labour turnover accords closely with their use of the term 'labour mobility' — that is, as a catch-all phrase for the flow of labour into and out of organisations.

At this juncture it is appropriate to comment on what, to us, constitutes mobility in the NHS, since it is not always a simple matter to classify someone as a joiner, stayer or leaver. The challenge is particularly acute in the instance of nurses because of the nature of their employment contract. Strictly speaking, nurses are employed by an Area Health Authority, although they usually work in a single hospital, in an individual health district. Where the nurse leaves the Area little problem is created, but confusion is more liable when the move is contained within that Area or District. In the latter case, formal termination of employment may not have occurred, although clearly a move has been made from one institution to another. Does this warrant categorisation as a 'leaver'? Our rule has been that the individual hospital is the 'employer', so that leaving corresponds to a relocation elsewhere, irrespective of whether the individual has joined another Health Authority. ('Joining' is the reverse of this.) However, even this codification does not eliminate all ambiguities. What, for example, of internal movement or transfer within a hospital — to another ward or unit, or a change in occupational status? Then again, it is sometimes awkward to gain acceptance on how far a particular hospital spreads. Some District General Hospitals comprise several sub-hospitals over a wide area — typically these are maternity or psychiatric units. In the resolution of these difficulties we have kept close to what nursing common sense told us, but inevitably arbitrary judgements have been made. We started from the proposition that all instances of handing in notice to quit constituted a separation. In addition, any nurses who left their original place of employment (hospital) are classified as leavers if the move to another institution or part of the same Health Authority lasted longer than a month. This last caveat allowed through the leavers' net those nurses who merely transfer to another institution or unit to help out — often during a temporary shortage of staff. It means, however, that some nurses are categorised as leavers although they have not formally handed in their notice, but excludes those who transfer within their organisation, irrespective of whether the move is in hours worked, shift, ward or grade. Nevertheless, we accept that some hospitals, such as the large teaching ones, are better placed to contain mobility as we have defined it since they have more scope to offer alternative posts. This 'move without moving' is something which we have tried to assess, although not within turnover rates, since we accept that there is a potential effect on these calculations. Our concentration on external (permanent) mobility does none the less separate our approach from those who regard termination of employment as a continuum of involvement or participation in the employing organisation. In the framework of March and Simon,[5] the employees who hand in their notice stand at one extreme of a continuum which also includes absenteeism, sickness and accidents as additional strategies available to reluctant workers. The exact nature of the relationship between these several forms of behaviour is much disputed, and although all have obvious relevance to nurse managers, we have excluded mention of any withdrawal action which does not result in leaving completely.[6]

If labour turnover is about the retention and movement of people in work, it is rather surprising that so little attention has been given to the direction in which people are going, or from whence they came initially. It is inexplicable to us that some restrict so drastically the notion of turnover to that movement which takes the worker from one place of employment to another. Again this is a quite unnecessary qualification, and one which prejudges by elimination the possibility that there may be some common elements in labour mobility despite the different directions taken. In a detailed classification, Parnes distinguishes between seven categories of labour movement as follows:

(1) Interfirm movement, from one firm to another or a change of employer.
(2) Occupational movement, from one occupation to another.
(3) Industrial movement, from one industry to another.
(4) Geographic movement, from one firm to another.
(5) Movement from an unemployed to an employed status.
(6) Movement from an employed to an unemployed status.
(7) Movement into and out of the labour force.[7]

In our own study of trained nurses, rather than restrict ourselves to what is called above 'inter-firm movement' — as many interpret their remit in a labour turnover project — we presume that our subjects may legitimately be mobile in any of the directions enumerated by Parnes. And this may be at their own, at their employer's, or at some other third party's initiative. To exclude, if nothing else, 'movement into and out of the labour force', as an aspect of nursing turnover when the majority of the research population are women is wholly unacceptable. For as we have previously mentioned, it has been an important element in the sexual division of labour that women are expected to alternate between paid employment and an exclusive concentration on work in the home.

Against Parnes' classification it cannot be taken for granted that all instances of labour mobility can be segregated neatly into one of the categories isolated. In many cases a specific move incorporates two or more of the dimensions so that it, for example, encloses a change of employer (firm), as well as of occupation, plus a geographic transfer to

another part of the country. This will present difficulties in
determining which, if any, of the several push/pull factors that have
been identified is pre-eminent. Nevertheless, with that proviso, we
believe that it is important that no study of labour turnover should
foreclose any of these several directional possibilities.

This focus on labour movement and retention, with its concern
for the direction taken, needs to be further supplemented by an
analysis of the conditions and reasons underlying this behaviour.
Again, it is curious that so much of the previous research in this area
has been reluctant, or has refused outright, to explore how those
involved interpret what they have done, and why. Surely it is as
significant to understand why a particular turnover rate exists, as to
be aware of its level? Unfortunately, to the extent that interest has
been exhibited, this has become stuck in those ubiquitous but
restrictive dichotomies: voluntary/involuntary, and controllable/
uncontrollable. In an attempt to combine these, Northcott identifies:
(1) voluntary separations, which are the act of the individual
(2) dismissals, for which management is responsible; and (3) unavoidable
separations, which he describes as 'self-explanatory'.[8] He goes on to
argue,

> Under the first heading will come such motives as the desire for
> personal betterment or dissatisfaction with the job and its pay and
> conditions. Dismissal may be the consequence of disciplinary
> offences, the unsuitability of the worker, or redundancy.
> 'Unavoidable' is a category which usually encompasses illness or
> accident, retirement, death, domestic responsibilities, leaving the
> district, military service and in the case of women, marriage and
> pregnancy.[9]

Despite the intent and formal appearance, this sort of approach in
reality only extracts all reason from the so-called 'reasons for leaving'
by the imposition of crude categories designed to be useful to
management. To take one illustration, the grouping of marriage with
death and military service as unavoidable reasons for leaving speaks
volumes for the blinkered and sterile approach assumed by too many
writers on personnel management and manpower planning. The linking
of so many heterogeneous elements totally ignores the social and
cultural location of the individuals involved, and how these may be
translated into reasons for what they have done. More specifically,
such an approach betrays an orientation which presumes that the

constituency under inspection is the male, manual worker in manufacturing industry — or that the problems of this group are mirrored in other sectors, such as female workers. We believe that it is for the investigator to explore the subtle nuances of meaning and significance which people ascribe to their overall life and work experiences and circumstances. Marriage is not necessarily an automatic death sentence as far as working as a nurse is concerned. It may be associated with some labour mobility, but this sort of relationship is the subject for investigation rather than the justification to bring any analysis to a quick full stop.

These strictures apply equally to the work of some sociologists as writers on personnel management. The problem is highlighted in what is otherwise a most circumspect and considered statement on labour turnover by Price.[10] He repeats the basic division into voluntary and involuntary turnover, and then superimposes a further distinction to differentiate between that part of the behaviour which is controllable and the remainder which is felt to lie beyond managerial intervention. The initial breakdown depends in this account on whether the decision to leave is at the instigation of the employer or the employee. (The concentration is always on leaving, since none of these writers regard those other aspects of turnover — joining or staying in an organisation — through the same voluntary/involuntary spectacles.) Not only is voluntary departure considered more amenable to managerial action, but Price argues that it is the prevalent form of turnover, with the exception perhaps in economic recessions. The list of responses which are viewed as involuntary, or not initiated by the worker, includes 'dismissals, lay-offs, retirement and deaths'.[11] The costs to the organisation seem to be a powerful test for the location of reasons in this category. 'There is less that managers can do to reduce the costs connected with lay-offs, retirements and deaths, for example, and it is natural for managers to focus on costs which are somewhat more controllable.'[12] Even if this categorisation strikes a sympathetic chord with managers, it hardly seems an appropriate starting point for social research. What exactly, one is entitled to ask, is 'controllability'? The category of 'involuntary-controllable' has little interest for Price, and yet Van der Merwe and Miller strongly advocate the inclusion of dismissals within labour turnover measurement and analysis. Indeed, they argue for the consideration of all dismissals — whether for reasons of indiscipline, or because of some other alleged unsuitability, which has led up to the enforced departure. This interpretation is supported by their own research in South Africa that uncovered a dismissal rate which acconted for almost one-half of total departures.[13]

The statements referred to here touch upon several immediate complications which ensue when the wider academic interest in work behaviour and attitudes is narrowed to make the research relevant to managers. In our view, this way is lined with many pitfalls. To illustrate the shortcomings of imposing a simple employer- or employee-initiated structure on all leavers, let us consider the specific case of those who report pregnancy as their reason for quitting. Once pregnant, the individual must give up work, but why not temporarily rather than permanently? Might not the provision of a creche turn the 'uncontrollable' loss into a short break from employment? And who exactly has determined that a decision to become pregnant is not affected by factors over which an employer is normally thought to exercise some influence? Quite simply, what is (in)voluntary turnover to one person is not regarded as such by the next. We prefer to describe our own study as an exploration of how, and under what conditions, the movement of labour occurs, without prior exclusion of instances of movement because they cannot allegedly be controlled by management. The process of joining and leaving a particular place of employment is amenable to a detailed phenomenological study, and while that term is not appropriate to our own discussion, we accept that labour turnover and the reasons which are offered by those involved — whether employees or employers — are socially organised. It has become commonplace to assert that concepts, like people, have careers, and labour turnover is no exception. What must be established from the outset is that commentators recognise that turnover exists in a particular social context, and that interested parties (whether academic or managerial) should refrain from the temptation to slot individuals into categories which fit their presumptions that such behaviour is only to be interpreted from the standpoint of the employing organisation. As long as that view persists, the interests of management will win out in terms of the criteria laid down for labelling turnover. We have already indicated the confused reasoning which treats voluntary/involuntary as valid or homogeneous categories, and this stems in large part from the uncertainty of reaction from other persons, both before and after the act has been committed. In short, these divisions are not based on a quality which resides in the behaviour itself, but in the ill-defined interaction between the person who leaves and some other interested observer(s).

We accept that, for the majority, the so-called decision to stay, join or leave is often played out in what Max Weber referred to as a state of 'inarticulate half-consciousness'. Nevertheless, we contend, it is a valuable and necessary exercise in labour turnover research to examine the reasons reported by those involved, as set within the wider context of their motivation to work. We do not minimise the substantial problems that attend such an enterprise. As C. Wright Mills, among others, pointed out,

> motives which are normally thought of as coming before action are in fact *post hoc* rationalisations; explanations advanced to explain actions in terms which are acceptable to one's own perceptions and, more important, intelligible to those whose opinions and reactions are felt to be important to oneself.[14]

Such doubts about individuals' own definition of their situation have encouraged another school of thinking which constructs a model of turnover without reference to the vocabulary of interested parties in the search for determinants of a different order.[15] Again we have adopted a rather uneasy compromise position. In this discussion labour turnover covers the movement of persons into and out of a specific place of employment. The direction and the conditions under which such mobility occurs are problematic and therefore integral parts of the investigation. Recruitment, retention and leaving are set against the broader context of experiences, motivations and social constraints which surround the nurse.

The Measurement of Labour Turnover

The inability of commentators to arrive at a consensus on the nature of labour turnover has had evident ramifications for its measurement. In practice, just as there is an abundance of definitions, so there is a welter of alternative measures. Thus even when the same data are under examination, quite contrary levels of turnover can be reported. Not only have the number of measures proliferated, but their complexity has been accentuated by the entry of statisticians into this area. The hive of activity which they have created has yet to produce a corresponding impact on the diagnosis and treatment of turnover, and our discussion will be concentrated on the various formulae for estimating rates of turnover, and probabilities of leaving, with 'real world' data.[16] We detect four main types of measure in the literature. Each of these illustrates a specific aspect of turnover, and only with their joint use will the building of a rounded perspective be achieved.

We shall focus on what each purports to measure, its appropriateness to that end, and finally, any problems of interpretation.[17] No claim is made that what follows comprises an exhaustive survey of turnover measures — the interested reader may consult several excellent reviews.[18] The four areas which we span are: (1) completed length of service (CLS) and associated averages; (2) crude turnover rates (of accession and separation); (3) cohort turnover rates (of stability and wastage); and (4) force of separation probabilities of staying/leaving.

Our sole excursion into turnover modelling is limited to several well known attempts to identify a distinctive pattern of turnover, most typically associated with specific stages or decisional states. But we accept that the aim must be to transform turnover rates into an explanatory model of the whole process. Hence our presumption that the basic ingredient of turnover research is knowledge about the overall work record and life cycle.

Completed Length of Service and Associated Averages

The distribution of completed length of service (employment) — whether in current (or previous) post, grade, hospital and so forth — is the typical starting point for most discussions of labour turnover. It permits graphic representation in a CLS curve, where length of employment is plotted against the proportion of the work-force who have accumulated that amount of service. From this, a simple calculation of average length of service is possible. The attraction of using one of the averages — mean, median or mode — is that the computation entails little mathematical sophistication, although each of these averages contains a source of potential bias. As most usually calculated, the measure is of average length of service in present post, although the reference point could just as easily be grade, hospital or nursing specialism, and so on.

$$\text{Average length of employment} = \frac{\text{Sum of individual employment lengths}}{\text{Number of employees}}$$

It is important to be as precise as possible in the specification of employment lengths, and most preferably these should not exceed one year. In our project, the information obtained from the nurses was sufficiently precise to enable us to make calculations on six-monthly intervals in the first year, although this was extended to a yearly basis for those with longer periods of service. The denominator comprised those nurses who provided information on employment record via questionnaires administered by us. Of course, further breakdown was possible to isolate selected subgroups as the need and interest dictated. The simplicity of calculation should not be allowed to mask the potential for distortion, as any statistics textbook will confirm.[19] With respect to the *mean*, this is suspect in that extreme items or subgroups at the margin may have a disproportionate effect. While a high average indicates a low level of turnover when looking at the group as a whole, this may disguise a considerable spread over both new recruits and very long-stay employees. This is significant because studies have, almost without exception, reported that it is the new recruits who provide a quite disproportionate number of leavers. One alternative, or supplement, to the mean is the *median* length of employment. This divides the group under inspection into equal parts, and on its own it carries little weight, although it copes well with non-symmetrical distributions and, as with all averages, it is more illuminating when used in conjunction with measures of central dispersion such as standard deviation or skewness. The third of the averages is the *mode*, which denotes the most frequently populated employment length. To its advantage, it is not affected by extreme values in the same way as the mean, although it does suffer from the drawback that, if the distribution does not show an overall concentration towards the|modal length, the claim to represent an average is scarcely legitimate. These deficiencies accepted, there is merit in calculating average length of employment figures, if only because of their popularity in previous research on labour turnover.

The CLS curve has received recent official backing in the rather specialised form of an 'index of stability' or as an 'index of skill conservation'. This measures the proportion of staff who have been with their current employer, or in their current post, for twelve months or more.[20] Its worth is enhanced, however, if the more heterogeneous proportion with more than one year's service can be broken down. To illustrate this point, if 50 per cent have accumulated at least 12 months' service, that group may contain a range between one and forty years, or may include no one with more than two years' continuous employment.

A further aspect to completed years of service in current post is the previous work record. This necessitates reference to the number and type of earlier jobs, the average time spent in each, and the number and duration of any breaks from work. For some, such information gives credence to the notion of a clearly defined work cycle, and this has been documented in the case of trained nurses.

In keeping with trends in the female labour force generally, more and more female nurses and midwives break their career at the birth of their first child, return when circumstances allow, often on a part-time basis in the first instance, and gradually increase the contribution they make to the profession as their children grow older. At present over a half of all married nurses and midwives return, in striking contradiction to casual impressions that most do not return. . .As might be expected, male nurses show rather different career characteristics from their female colleagues. Few, of course, work part-time. Even more significant, they tend to enter nursing somewhat later in life and are more likely to have had previous experience of other work. Once trained, however, the proportion who leave the service is lower than the corresponding figure for female nurses, largely because there is no temporary drop-out in mid-career.[21]

Crude Turnover Rates

The standard elaboration of a turnover rate is developed by Brissenden and Frankel in their search for a method which incorporated almost every aspect of the ebb and flow of people into and out of an organisation. We have allied our concern for the direction, and reasons underlying mobility, to their distinction between recruitment, replacement and departures.[22] The main areas that provoke controversy are illustrated in Figure 2.1, and extend across both numerator and denominator. First, in the numerator, some advocate a separation of recruits depending on whether they are replacements for, or additions to, existing staff. On the leavers side, the rate may be broken down according to the reasons for leaving. This is supplemented by reference to the direction followed in any departure. On the other side, it is usual to take as the base figure something on the theme of the 'number in employment'. Yet the size of the work-force may be calculated on the basis of the number of persons employed, or the number of worker-hours — where, for example, allowance is made for absence — of whatever sort. Brissenden and Frankel were adamant that measurements should be sensitive to changes in the number of worker-hours. If, for instance, the denominator declined markedly over a particular time period, the loss of the same number of workers automatically generates a rising rate of turnover. The most regularly used corrective has been to use the average number employed over a specific time period as the base, rather than setting the denominator as the figure

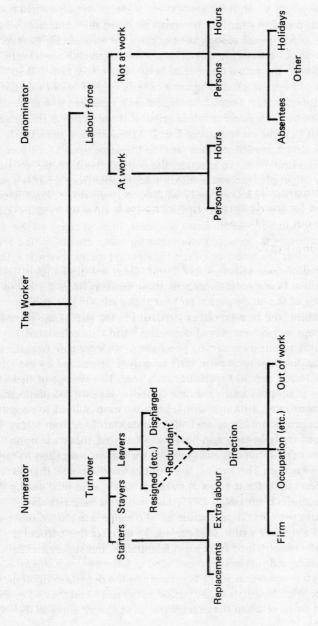

Figure 2.1: Schematic Representation of Factors used in the Calculation of Crude Turnover Rates

Source: Based on J.D. Hackett, *Labor Management* (New York, 1929), p.311.

in employment when the investigation began, or perhaps when it ended.

In our own investigation the composition of the numerator was quite straightforward as long as hospitals kept an accurate staff record — which was not always the case. The number of starters, or leavers, was equated with the actual number of persons involved, rather than number of hours worked. The same criteria applied in our calculation of the denominator. Despite Brissenden and Frankel's powerful strictures, considerable confusion reigns if those in hospitals are asked to accept that the movement of four 0.25 whole-time equivalents (WTEs), that is part-timers, amounts to the same thing as the turnover of one full-time nurse. In practice, the concentration on the actual number of people involved, while not acceptable from a purist's point of view, will merge more closely with the way in which turnover is experienced in nursing. But we shall footnote turnover rates in terms of worker-hours for comparative purposes. In most respects, the specification of the denominator raises the same issues — plus a few more besides. The question of the time period under review is rather more troublesome with the base figure. There are three main alternatives. One can establish how many workers there are at the beginning of the study period (t^1), or at the end (t^2), or as a compromise, and to even out any changes in the size of the work-force, the average number employed between t^1 and t^2 is calculated.

Turning to our own nursing population, we were able to make use of official hospital returns on staff employed demanded by the DHSS as of 31 March and 30 September each year. The average of these two figures was adopted as the baseline figure in our own calculations of recruitment rates, although with leavers we were obliged to adopt a different procedure. Since we had accurate staff lists from 1 May 1975 (when our study began), and because our central focus was upon movement from that original group, there was no obligation to take corrective action. This means, to re-emphasise the point, that our crude separation rate is for the loss of nurses from those in post during the twelve months from 1 May 1975. This will underestimate the departures over that time because no allowance is made for those who join and also leave within that period. To counter this particular deficiency we obtained from most hospitals in our survey the data on these losses, and this has been included in what has been described as a 'corrected separation rate'. This refers to the departure of all nurses from specified hospitals in the period between t^1 and t^2, and in this instance we have taken the average size of the work-force as the baseline.

$$\text{Recruitment rate (per cent)} = \frac{\text{Number of recruits } (t^1 \text{ to } t^2)}{\text{Number of workers}} \times 100$$

$$\text{Separation rate (per cent)} = \frac{\text{Number of leavers } (t^1 \text{ to } t^2)}{\text{Number of workers}} \times 100$$

This means that the sub-categories of separation and recruitment, which comprise the crude turnover rate, contain only the basic ingredients illustrated in Figure 2.1. To its considerable advantage, the crude turnover rate in its bowdlerised form is most easy to compute, and will be similarly undemanding in terms of the data on which it is based. But this discussion cannot be left without mentioning its well versed shortcoming.[23] Thus, a separation rate of 100 per cent can mean one of several things: (1) that the entire work-force has left; (2) that one half of the work-force has been replaced twice; (3) that a quarter has turned over on four occasions, and so on. Much of the confusion has stemmed from the too ready acceptance of measures which have their origin in demographic analysis — where basic assumptions about a fairly steady flow each year in births and deaths rings true with actual experience.[24] But as Silcock has cogently illustrated, the character of labour turnover that has been widely accepted emphasises that the CLS curve is always skewed towards those with short service. This prevents a direct comparison of turnover rates, since those organisations which have just recruited in significant numbers will typically exhibit a relatively higher level of separations. This characteristic may be countered in part by including a breakdown of the population according to important features, if not by directly controlling for length of service. The potential for confounding factors to assert themselves in the crude turnover rate does again spotlight the need to use this measure in conjunction with others, if not to concentrate on those techniques which contain an in-built control for length of service, such as the cohort turnover rates. However, the crude turnover rate has dominated the literature and we feel obliged to include it in order to allow scope for comparing the record of our nursing population with that reported among other groups.

Cohort Turnover Rates

Cohort turnover rates concentrate upon a group of new entrants to an organisation. By such means a particular cohort may be followed through for the duration of their stay. The computation merely demands some indication of how many members of each cohort have left, or remain, after specified time periods — usually six months, one year, two years and so forth. Two distinct types of measure based on this approach have gained usage, according to Price.[25] These are the stability/instability rates, and the survival/wastage rates.[26] The survival rates differ from the stability versions in that they consider only those in the cohort at entry, while the latter operate with the size of the work-force as their base figure. In our opinion this renders the survival rate a far superior instrument. It means that a wastage rate of 100 per cent describes only one possible eventuality — where every single member of the cohort has left the organisation. Thus, not only does the survival rate control for length of service, but it conveys an exact record of what is happening to the group under inspection. In complete contrast, the stability rates almost defy easy interpretation, and we have therefore chosen to ignore them in this discussion.

$$\frac{\text{Survival/wastage}}{\text{rate (per cent)}} = \frac{\text{Number in cohort who stay/leave, } t^1 \text{ to } t^2}{\text{Number in cohort}} \times 100$$

The cohort method does not extinguish all difficulties in the measurement of turnover — needless to say. Most obviously, problems can arise in the definition of a cohort, or in the establishment of the cut-off points which determine whether a worker is placed in one cohort or another. This burden of assignment is compounded where the volume of recruits into the organisation is low. And with respect to nurses, it has been generally claimed that there was a noteworthy decline in labour mobility in the mid-1970s.[27] In consequence, we were obliged to construct cohorts equivalent to entry over four-month intervals. Again the essence of such analysis involves the tracing of entrants over an extended time period over several years, but such was the paucity of accurate staff records in hospitals that we were restricted in this ambition. Most adherents to cohort analysis attach special significance to the time taken for a cohort to be reduced by one-half — the so-called 'half-life' — but so restricted were our data sources and so depleted were nursing departures, that none of the cohorts identified in our study declined by that magic amount. The other significant qualification against cohort analysis is that its sole concern with new recruits will provide an underestimation of the absolute level of departures, at least until the research has been going on long enough to include every employee in a cohort. Since few organisations have such complete information, this again emphasises the need to operate a variety of turnover measures.

Force of Separation

The last area of measurement is more strictly an estimation of the probability of leaving rather than a rate of turnover. It comprises a transitional probability of leaving (or staying) for those who have already achieved a stated length of service in the ensuing time period. The technique has been adopted almost root and branch from demographic analysis, where it has long been a standard method of calculation. Just as demographers distinguish between an average life expectancy that may be estimated for, say, all men and women, and a life expectancy figure which is related to whether the person is seven years old or seventy, so too a comparable distinction may be applied in turnover research. In this case the contrast is between an average length of service and its associated completed length of service curve, and a force of separation probability. The latter is calculated in the knowledge that the individual has already been in the organisation for a specified time period, and this enables one to provide a much more precise picture of the likelihood of departure.

We have calculated the force of separation by dividing the number of leavers with a particular length of service in their current post by all nurses with that time in employment. Our information on groups of cohorts has been limited by available hospital records, and we have therefore applied the force of separation calculations to the census-type, or cross-sectional data in addition to the cohorts of new entrants. Despite the practical difficulties in obtaining information of sufficient quality to enable force of separation calculations to be made, the effort is repaid by the sophistication of the technique. Indeed, of all the measures discussed it seems the best suited to stand on its own. Its main feature is that it compensates for the disadvantage of the typical cross-sectional techniques, such as the completed length of service, or the crude turnover rate, by controlling for length of service. Furthermore it goes further than cohort rates, by directing attention to the whole process of turnover — from recruitment through to eventual departure. In so doing, it transforms the survival rates of cohort analysis into unambiguous probabilities of continued presence in the organisation.

Models of Labour Turnover as a Social Process

The complement to the various turnover measures is the attempt to generate explanatory models of the form of turnover. The intention is to identify an underlying regularity in the movement of people through

an organisation. This quest has been most obviously stimulated by the
pioneering studies conducted by researchers of the Tavistock Institute
in the 1940s at the Glacier Metal Company.[28] Their conclusion was
that there were certain 'basic social processes' operating in labour
turnover. Despite the considerable dislocation of industry as a result
of the Second World War, and the immediate aftermath, the
fluctuations in employment were short-term and 'there remained a level
of turnover which was relatively constant for the institution in which it
occurred'.[29] They then describe a survival curve which contains three
clearly identifiable phases or critical points through which 'any group of
entrants must pass':

(a) the period of induction crisis, during which a certain number of
   casualties results from the first mutual interaction between the
   engaging company and the entrant group;
(b) the period of differential transit, during which those who have
   survived learn the ways of the company and discover how far
   they have a place in it;
(c) the period of settled connection, when those who have survived
   the first two periods take on the character of quasi-permanent
   employees.[30]

Turnover as a social process is summed up by the phrase 'an employee
begins to leave when he enters, and continues to enter until he leaves'.[31]
The actual time scale over which these stages unfold varies between
organisations. In the case of the Glacier Metal Company, the Tavistock
team reported that the induction crisis lasted characteristically for a few
weeks or months, with a five-week period being the norm. Its end is
signalled by the rapid decline in the number of departures from the firm.
It is followed by a period of differential transit which may well extend
over several years — a figure of 255 weeks is mentioned in the Glacier
study. The dividing line between this and the ensuing stage of a settled
connection is established at the point where the number leaving in
successive time intervals holds steady. The process is represented
diagrammatically in Figure 2.2.

   The basic notion of the survival curve in the Tavistock model is
further elaborated by Hill, where he refers to labour turnover as a
'quasi-stationary' process.[32] By this he means that in the short term the
basic profile of the curve may be distorted, but that despite such
disturbances, the rate of separation returns to its previous level. That is
to say, homeostasis is an integral feature of labour turnover. Within this

Figure 2.2: The 'Tavistock Model' of Turnover

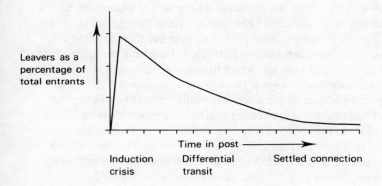

model individuals are confronted by a series of decisions about their continuation in the organisation. The crucial question revolves around the association between service length and leaving probability. This has encouraged many attempts to formulate dynamic statistical models of the turnover process. For example, Silcock sees the following implications in the Tavistock model:

> The movements from entrant to leaver is regarded as continuous; the rate at which it proceeds is constant; this constant rate reflects and is determined by the characteristics of each individual firm; and finally, if the rate is disturbed by temporary extraneous forces it tends to revert to its former level when these forces cease to operate.[33]

Silcock's examination of the critical assumption of a constant force of separation, and the negative exponential distribution to which it leads, is most dismissive. The fit to actual data is so imperfect that 'no appeal to any statistical test is required'.[34] If people's work behaviour contradicts basic assumptions in the Tavistock model, what other possibilities are there? Silcock himself proposes that, '(1) the interaction between the characteristics of the employing company and the characteristics of the individual employee results in a constant force of separation. . .; (2) (this). . .varies from one employee to another', with a given probability distribution.[35] We are sympathetic to an approach which allows that the retention of an individual employee is not decided simply by the actions of the employer, but more typically as a result of the interaction between employer and employee. Yet this view suffers from the implausible premiss that individuals have a constant force of separation that remains fixed throughout their stay with a particular organisation, if not throughout their working life. Rather too often contributions in this area have been turned into abstract statistical exercises which have lost their way in attempting to order an individual's progress through an organisation.[36] While we accept the plethora of formidable stumbling blocks to this type of model-building, some interesting explanatory possibilities have been opened up in the so-called 'time dependent' or decision-making examples, which are essentially a variation on the Tavistock theme. For example, Herbst has talked of several transitional states through which employees pass.[37] These are represented in Figure 2.3.

In Herbst's model, the constants, K1. . .K5, represent what he refers to as 'transformation probabilities' or 'intensities'. These relate to the intensity demonstrated in an individual's movement from one level of commitment to another. Thus a high intensity refers to a strong probability of movement, while a low intensity is associated with remaining in an organisation. Again we are confronted with an

Figure 2.3: Herbst's Decision Process Model of Turnover

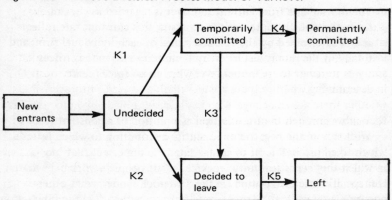

apparently unrealised propostion that the same set of intensities
applies to each and every worker within a particular organisation, at
each stage, although variation will typically exist across the several
decisional states. Thus there will be contrasts in the force of separation
across individuals because people will be at different stages in their
career through the organisation. Furthermore, Herbst suggests that
different intensities will arise in different organisations. This means
that individuals will display several transformation probabilities as they
move from one organisation to another. Once more reports of excellent
match between model and empirical data create the impression of a
gulf between statistical confidence and the easy translation of such
regularities into convincing social explanations of the turnover process.
As Stainer caustically observes, Herbst's model 'implies a facility of
communication between individuals which has never been observed in
other fields of human activity'.[38] While we accept that Herbst's model
does highlight crucial problems for the study of labour turnover, we
start from the premiss that the orientation to work is the product of a
more considerable yet less constant range of factors than he is willing
to admit. If this creates chaos for statistical modelling, then so be it.
We are certainly dubious about claims that individuals move inexorably
from a state of chronic hesitancy to one of a settled connection, or else
leave in one of the intervening stages. For us, individuals may retrace
their steps in terms of their commitment to the organisation. Yet in
Herbst's model 'permanently committed' and 'decided to leave' have
the air of terminal states. Again, people may join an organisation
without any intention of remaining for more than a few months, and
therefore the 'undecided' category is not a state through which all
necessarily pass. In broader terms, such models very much describe a
group with little distractions to their career, and for this reason the
situation of a predominantly female work-force is not easily merged
into the key decisions which confront those in Herbst's model. In our
study of nursing we are therefore very much at a preliminary position
in determining whether there are identifiable stages of turnover, and
whether these are associated with key decisions made by individuals as
they move through the organisation.

  With this in mind we included questions for our nursing respondents
which fixed on their level of commitment to the particular organisation
in which they were currently working, as well as to the profession itself.
Our specific interest focused on the manner in which views expressed at
one time are matched by subsequent behaviour, or whether opinions
change in an 'unexpected' manner.

Figure 2.4: Intention of Movement Possibilities, t^1 to t^2

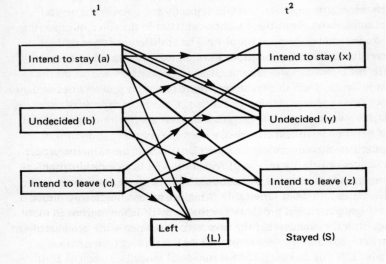

The possibilities illustrated in Figure 2.4 are that the individual nurses may move from one of the expressed positions a, b, or c at the time of the initial contact either out of the organisation entirely (to L), or if they remain, to one of the main commitment levels, under S. This does not mean that we accept the existence of a simple chain reaction — reasons for leaving. . .decision to leave. . .actual departure. But we acknowledge that labour turnover research must adopt a longer time perspective than has usually been evident. The goal is to trace a person through their stay in an organisation, and indeed across several organisations through their working life. We anticipate that individuals enter employment with certain experiences and expectations which help form an orientation to work that is itself transformed as the situation in which they find themselves changes. Any crises in work are likely to be more acute for the novitiate than for the long-serving employee, but successful navigation of the initial entry period does not mean an end to socialisation and adjustment. There will be repeated self-questioning about the decision to stay in, or leave, one's job or employer. Hence, the probability of leaving an organisation is not fixed but is instead a function of employment hopes and experiences, and the structural conditions and constraints within which that individual is operating.

This also sets our approach against that parallel mode of exposition which translates the force of separation into a psychological trait. Individuals are then treated as the carriers of specific propensities, operationalised as personality characteristics, which determine individual employment lengths. In several respects this formulation corresponds closely to an explanation popular with many personnel managers. This divides the work-force into two main categories: first, there are the 'drifters' or 'flitters' whose behaviour consists of frequent movement between jobs, or in and out of work; and secondly, there are the more solid and stable group of loyal 'stayers' whose personality is conducive to the formation of a lasting attachment to their employing organisation, and to their work colleagues. The former are associated with a lower level of reliability − both as individuals and as workers. These stereotypes exist in nursing as much as other occupations. It is not necessarily that the drifters consciously prefer their work-style, but they leave almost in spite of themselves. In more esoteric statistical circles they have been compared with 'accident prone' persons; and this has encouraged the search for something akin to a 'leaver's chromosome'. We feel it sufficient to mention here that much of the criticism directed against the notion of a constant force of separation is equally applicable when the model assumes a psychological basis. To take one illustration: the assertion that an individual has a given propensity to leave means that this person will stay/depart with equal alacrity − whatever the employer, and whatever the individual's social circumstances. There is much evidence to cast serious doubts on this assertion; indeed the very relationship of leaving with length of service and age contradict the direct effect of personality types. In practice, individuals are known to become more stable in their work habits as they get older, and there are sound non-psychological reasons why this should be.[39] It is equally unhelpful, however, to go to the other extreme and to deny that some individuals display a much higher level of mobility than is the norm. But the explanation for this does not rest exclusively, or even pre-eminently, in the psyches of those individuals. Personality tests, like careful induction programmes, may have some success in identifying those who tend to leave in the early months of employment, but they have been far less successful in pinpointing the long-stay employees. There are additional complications in an occupation like nursing which further militate against the identification of leavers on personality grounds. Most obviously, trained nurses have all undergone at least two years' training and have an informed, realistic view of what to expect in nursing. Moreover, on qualification, nurses enter an occupation where some mobility is encouraged by the authorities. Of course there are many other reasons which could be mentioned — suffice to record that we have not delved into the relationship between personality and labour mobility.

Our Study Design

We shall complete our review of the nature and measurement of labour turnover with a brief outline of the design of our own research into nursing turnover.[40]

Our study is based on a sample of trained nursing staff in District General Hospitals in Yorkshire. We do not claim to have drawn a representative sample of qualified nurses, and therefore there is no statistical justification for extending the remarks offered here to any group beyond those enumerated. By trained staff we mean those enrolled and registered nurses who occupy the following grades: (a) state enrolled nurse (SEN), which includes senior enrolled nurses; (b) staff nurses; and (c) ward sisters and their male equivalents, charge nurses. (Henceforward we shall refer to this group solely as ward sisters.) We quite deliberately sought to compare turnover between grades, but it was decided to exclude pupil and student nurses — in part because their inclusion would have greatly increased the size of the study, and in part because their plight has already been widely researched.[41] In addition, the problems they face at work are of a different order to those confronting trained staff, while we assume that the latter will have overcome the initial shocks of hospital life, and will not therefore be plunged into the sort of 'induction crisis' which awaits new trainees. If the lower limit was derived in this way, a similar reasoning led to the exclusion of all administrative grades of nurse, who were even more obviously engaged in a qualitatively different work regime.

All full-time staff from these grades who were in post on 1 May 1975 were included in our study. In addition, in three of the nine Districts covered, we contacted all part-time staff from the same three grades The latter could not be included in every hospital because of the massive increase in the size of the study that this would have necessitated. We further restricted our investigation to nurses at work in District General Hospitals. Previous projects have demonstrated the sort of variation that arises between the different types of hospital.[42] But again, to control for the multiplicity of categories of hospital in the NHS would have over-extended our meagre resources. As it is, the hospitals included in our survey comprised both new purpose-built units, as well as Victorian buildings spread over a considerable geographical area. Indeed sometimes the official designation of what constituted the District General Hospital (DGH) seemed to us and to the nurses employed there as untenable. In several instances therefore we accepted the *de facto* split of a single institution into separate hospitals, and hence we supposed that some Districts contain more than one DGH. The final tally is fourteen hospitals, which are spread throughout the large urban conurbations, as well as the rural hinterland. They include both teaching and non-teaching hospitals.

The data collected on these nurses originated in four main areas. First, a self-administered questionnaire was sent to all nurses in our sample who were in post on 1 May 1975 (see Appendix). In all, over 1,400 nurses, or approximately 70 per cent of those contacted, returned the questionnaire. This provided the basic data base for the whole study.[43] In addition, a similar questionnaire was sent to those nurses who remained in post over the ensuing twelve months; and for these stayers, a response rate of 66 per cent was achieved.[44] Secondly, we also collected a considerable volume of more qualitative material from personal interviews. The main thrust of the field-work during the period between May 1975 and May 1976 was towards those nurses whom we categorised as leavers, and 149 of these were interviewed. A very similar schedule was administered to some 78 stayers. The other two sources of data in our study were hospital records and informal contact and observation in hospitals. The first of these provided the most weighty contribution, and was absolutely essential in the calculation of several of the turnover rates — especially for recruitment.

To summarise the results of our data collection in this study: we obtained over 1,400 first-wave questionnaires, and more than 1,000 of the original population of nurses replied to a follow-up version a year later. In addition, over 225 personal interviews were conducted with stayers and leavers. Also, hospital records provided a wide range of official statistics on the recruitment and retention of nursing staff. Indeed the problem has not been one of a shortage of material for analysis, but how to order the veritable mountain of data into a relatively coherent and comprehensive framework that illustrated the several facets of nursing turnover.

Summary

In this chapter we have outlined the scope of our investigation of labour turnover among trained nurses. This comprises the movement of people into, between and out of positions of employment. The initial task is to specify the rate of turnover, but in practice, its several sides, and the shortcomings apparent in most of the standard techniques, demand that more than one measure is used. In addition, due allowance must be given to the direction of movement. With these points in mind, we now turn to illustrate, with material from our own case study, the level and variation in nursing turnover.

Notes

1. R. Hyman, 'Economic Motivation and Labour Stability', *British Journal of Industrial Relations*, vol.8 (1970), p.178.

2. R. Van der Merwe and S. Miller, 'The Measurement of Labour Turnover: a Critical Appraisal and a Suggested New Approach', *Human Relations*, vol.24 (1971), pp.233-53.

3. P.F. Brissenden and E. Frankel, *Labour Turnover in Industry: a Statistical Analysis* (Macmillan, New York, 1922).

4. Ibid., p.7.

5. J.G. March and H.A. Simon, *Organisations* (Wiley, New York, 1958).

6. See S. Redfern, 'Absence and Wastage in Trained Nurses: a Selective Review of the Literature', *Journal of Advanced Nursing*, vol.3 (1978), pp.231-49.

7. H.S. Parnes, *Research on Labour Mobility* (SSRC, New York, 1954), p.24.

8. C. Northcott, *Personnel Management*, 4th edn. (Pitman, London, 1968).

9. Ibid., p.268.

10. J. Price, 'A Theory of Turnover' in B.O. Pettman (ed.), *Labour Turnover and Retention* (Gower Press, London, 1975), ch.3.

11. Ibid., p.53.

12. Ibid., p.53.

13. Van der Merwe and Miller, 'The Measurement of Labour Turnover', pp.233-53.

14. C. Wright Mills, *The Sociological Imagination* (Penguin, Harmondsworth, 1970).

15. A.K. Rice, J.M. Hill and E.L. Trist, 'The Representation of Labour Turnover as a Social Process', *Human Relations*, vol.3 (1950), pp.349-72.

16. D.J. Bartholomew (ed.), *Manpower Planning* (Penguin, Harmondsworth, 1976).

17. G. Mercer and A. Long, 'Turnover of Labour in Nursing – Part 1', *Health Services Manpower Review*, no.3 (1977), pp.8-18; A. Long and G. Mercer, 'Turnover of Labour in Nursing – Part 2', *Health Services Manpower Review*, no.4 (1977), pp.6-10.

18. W.J. Byrt, 'Methods of Measuring Labour Turnover', *Personnel Practice Bulletin*, vol.13 (1957), pp.6-14; F.J. Gaudet, *Labour Turnover: Calculation and Cost*, Research Study no.39 (American Management Association, New York, 1970); J.L. Price, 'The Measurement of Turnover', *Industrial Relations*, vol.6 (1975/6), pp.34-46.

19. H.M. Blalock, *Social Statistics* (McGraw-Hill, New York, 1960), ch.5.

20. Department of Employment, *New Earnings Survey 1975* (HMSO, London, 1976). While both the Index of Stability and the Index of Skill Conservation employ as their numerators the number with 12 months' service plus, the former uses the number in post one year ago as the denominator, and the latter is based on the total employed now.

21. A. Briggs (Chairman), *Report of the Committee on Nursing* (HMSO, London, 1972), Cmnd. 7115, p.121.

22. Brissenden and Frankel, *Labour Turnover in Industry*, chs. 1 and 2. See also Price, 'The Measurement of Turnover', pp.37-8.

23. A.M. Bowey, 'Labour Stability Curves and a Labour Stability Index', *British Journal of Industrial Relations*, vol.7 (1969),|pp.71-83; H. Silcock, 'The Phenomenon of Labour Turnover', *Journal of the Royal Statistical Society*, Series A, vol.117 (1954), pp.429-40.

24. T.F. Greenwood, 'Problems of Industrial|Organisation', *Journal of the Royal Statistical Society*, vol.82 (1919), pp.186-209.

25. J. Price, 'The Measurement of Turnover', pp.39-43; M. Hedberg, *The Process of Labour Turnover*, Report no.52 (Swedish Council for Personnel Administration, Stockholm, 1967).

26. My reluctance to talk in terms of 'wastage' in this study withers before the admirable attempt at standardisation of terms expounded in J.L. Price, *The Study of Turnover* (Iowa State University Press, Iowa, 1977).

27. G. Mercer, 'Fluctuations over Time in the Rate of Nursing Turnover', unpublished paper, University of Leeds, 1978.

28. A.K. Rice, J.M. Hill and E.L. Trist, 'The Representation of Labour Turnover as a Social Process', *Human Relations*, vol.3 (1950), pp.349-72; J.M. Hill, 'A Consideration of Labour Turnover as a Resultant of a Quasi-stationary Process', *Human Relations*, vol.4 (1951), pp.255-64; A.K. Rice, 'The Relative Independence of Sub-institutions as Illustrated by Departmental Labour Turnover', *Human Relations*, vol.5 (1952), pp.89-90; A.K. Rice and E.L. Trist, 'Institutional and Sub-institutional Determinants of Change in Labour Turnover', *Human Relations*, vol.5 (1952), pp.347-71; J.M. Hill, *The Seafaring Career: a Study of the Forces Affecting Joining, Serving and Leaving the Merchant Navy* (Tavistock Institute, London, 1972).

29. Rice, Hill and Trist, 'The Representation of Labour Turnover as a Social Process', p.371.

30. Ibid., p.359.

31. Ibid., p.356.

32. Hill, 'A Consideration of Labour Turnover as a Quasi-stationary Process'.

33. Silcock, 'The Phenomenon of Labour Turnover', p.433.

34. Ibid., p.433.

35. Ibid., p.434.

36. For a variety of statistically oriented studies see Bartholomew, *Manpower Planning*, chs. 6-13; D.J. Bryant, 'A Survey of the Development of Manpower Planning Policies', *British Journal of Industrial Relations*, vol.3 (1965), pp.279-90; J. Lawrence, 'Manpower and Personnel Models in Britain', *Personnel Review*, vol.2 (1973), pp.4-27.

37. P.G. Herbst, 'Organisational Commitment: a Decision Process Model', *Acta Sociologica*, vol.7 (1963), pp.34-45.

38. G. Stainer, *Manpower Planning* (Heinemann, London, 1971), p.207.

39. M. Hedberg, *The Process of Labor Turnover,* Report no.52 (Swedish Council for Personnel Administration, Stockholm, 1967).

40. See G. Mercer and C. Mould, *An Investigation into the Level and Character of Labour Turnover amongst Trained Nurses*, Report for the DHSS (University of Leeds, 1976).

41. J.M. MacGuire, *Threshold to Nursing*, Occasional Papers on Social Administration, no.30 (Bell, London, 1969).

42. Central Health Services Council, *The Functions of the District General Hospital* (HMSO, London, 1969); Briggs, *Report of the Committee on Nursing*, ch.5.

43. A fuller account of the characteristics of the nurses in this study is contained in Mercer and Mould, *An Investigation into the Level and Character of Labour Turnover among Trained Nurses*, ch.6.

44. The first-wave questionnaire (Appendix) is based on a version developed by Professor J. Price (J. Price, *The Study of Turnover*), although this was considerably modified and supplemented in several important respects to make it appropriate for our investigation of British nurses.

3 THE LEVEL AND DIRECTION OF NURSING TURNOVER

In this chapter we begin our presentation of the material collected in our case study of labour turnover among trained nursing staff in NHS hospitals. The first step is to specify the general level of mobility, and secondly, to highlight some of the possibilities for internal variation in this rate. Discussions of nursing turnover generally focus on the following dimensions: (a) grade; (b) sex of nurse; (c) hours worked; and (d) hospital where currently employed. Needless to say, these do not constitute a final list of the factors which induce variation in nursing turnover, but all have been accorded significance within the profession.[1] They span a range of both work and non-work influences, and therefore provide a basic structure for the more detailed account of the determinants of nursing turnover which is pursued in Chapter 4. Here, we start with an assessment of the rate of nursing turnover as indicated by the several measures previously outlined.

Completed Length of Service and Associated Averages

The initial perspective on the nurses' work record is derived from the completed length of service figures. These encompass both the CLS curve (see Figure 3.1) as well as the various averages and measures of central dispersion (standard deviation), and of the 'peakedness' of the distribution (kurtosis) (see Table 3.1). While this section concentrates on the length of service in the current post, we shall supplement this with a parallel view of the previous work history of these nurses. This covers the number of posts held and the average stay, as well as the continuity of employment in nursing.

The overwhelming impression that we gain is of a work-force which comprises predominantly recent recruits who are concentrated in the shorter lengths of employment. Some 37 per cent of all respondents have been in their current post for less than one year, while 80 per cent have less than five years' service. A mere 6 per cent have accumulated more than ten years' continuous service in the same hospital. Among the averages, the overall modal figure is 1.5 years in post, the median spell is marginally higher at 1.7 years, but the mean length of employment extends noticeably to 3.1 years. That the averages are ordered in this way indicates that the CLS distribution peaks very

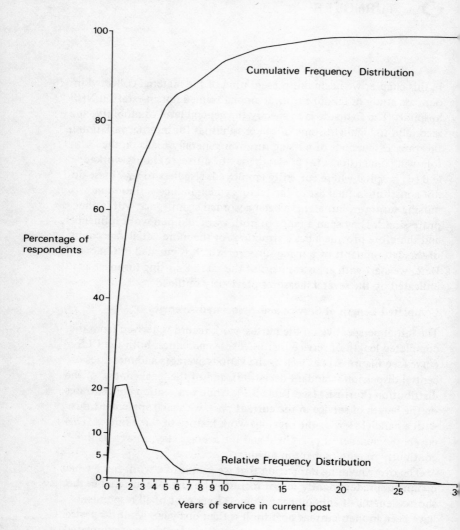

Figure 3.1: Completed Length of Service in Current Post (All Nurses)

Cumulative Frequency Distribution

Percentage of respondents

Relative Frequency Distribution

Years of service in current post

Table 3.1: Average Number of Years of Completed Service in Current Post (All Nurses)

	Mean	Median	Mode	Standard deviation	Kurtosis	N[a]
All	3.1	1.7	1.5	4.2	10.4	1,384
Grade						
SEN	3.4	2.1	1.5	4.0	12.2	357
SN	1.6	0.9	0.75	2.4	19.8	409
WS/CN	4.0	2.0	1.5	5.0	6.5	618
Hours						
FT	3.0	1.5	1.5	4.3	11.4	1,145
PT	3.7	2.5	2.5	3.8	3.3	239
Sex						
Female	3.0	1.7	1.5	3.9	9.8	1,253
Male	4.2	1.6	0.75	6.5	5.2	131
Hospitals						
A	2.3	1.5	0.75	2.7	13.9	119
B	2.6	1.6	0.75	2.7	2.1	36
C	3.2	1.1	0.75	4.8	7.5	79
D	3.0	1.3	0.75	4.9	11.6	90
E	2.6	1.5	1.50	4.6	23.7	40
F	2.8	2.3	2.50	2.3	1.7	53
G	4.0	1.8	1.50	5.3	4.9	58
H	4.0	2.5	2.50	4.8	8.2	139
I	3.1	1.6	0.75	3.8	4.1	106
J	5.7	3.9	1.50	6.1	3.1	71
K	2.8	1.1	0.25	4.5	10.2	185
L	2.9	1.7	1.50	3.4	5.4	208
M	2.9	1.6	0.75	4.4	12.3	125
N	2.5	1.7	1.50	2.6	4.5	75

a — No answer (N = 28) excluded.

All figures calculated at yearly intervals except in first year when divided into half years.

early and declines with almost equal speed, although a relatively small number of nurses are spread very thinly over a much elongated 'tail'. This is graphically illustrated in Figure 3.1, and in Table 3.1. Taken in conjunction, these features describe what in an unfortunate statistical mouthful comprises a positively skewed, unimodal, leptokurtic distribution; which, being translated, means that there is considerable movement among trained nurses, although there is a long-serving minority who inject some semblance of continuity into the picture.[2]

This predominance of short-service employees in the aggregate is also repeated in selected subgroups. In respect of grade, differences between enrolled and registered staff are fairly predictable. The potential for promotion and a career in the profession, which is reinforced by some official encouragement of movement between hospitals, that is enjoyed by registered nurses contrasts with the lack of such incentives among their enrolled colleagues. While a category of senior state enrolled nurse has been introduced, it covers a small fraction of the enrolled group (less than 12 per cent for England and Wales as a whole), and since it is largely a reward for long service, stability is the watchword. In consequence, SENs are presumed to be more inclined to remain in their current post, or to leave nursing entirely. Although the frequency of movement and length of service will also depend on the number of vacancies, the indications are of a relatively shorter length of service among registered nurses, especially staff nurses, because of their more ample opportunities for inter-hospital movement. A comparison of the average length of employment statistics in Table 3.1 partly supports these expectations. The outstanding feature is the exceptionally brief length of employment demonstrated by staff nurses. Over 60 per cent have spent less than a year in their current post, 94 per cent less than five years, while no full-time staff nurse has filled the same position for more than ten years. However, their colleagues in the registered grades — ward sisters and charge nurses — and enrolled staff present a more settled picture. Ward sisters are dispersed in relatively greater numbers above the five-year mark, and have a higher mean length of service, and this places them much closer to enrolled nurses than their staff nurse juniors. To illustrate this point, the mean figures descend from 4.0 years for ward sisters, through 3.4 years among enrolled nurses, then plummet to a low of 1.6 years for staff nurses. While this pattern confirms the high instability of the latter, it also demonstrates that, once in the ward sister grade, registered nurses are converted to a more stable life.

Part-time staff are another group which is widely believed to display a distinctive work profile — irrespective, in the case of trained nurses, of their grade. The reasons usually advanced dwell upon the factors which led them to choose part-time employment in the first place. Typically, part-timers are keen to obtain a paid job and get away from the house, but the same domestic commitments alternatively inhibit and promote labour turnover. On the one hand, this group is not well placed to further their career in nursing, since the opportunities for movement between hospitals are severely restricted by their home circumstances and furthermore, as part-timers, they occupy a relatively disadvantaged position in the promotion stakes. On the other hand, their domestic circumstances are relatively more likely to propel them out of work altogether. The latter pressures militate against a high CLS and on balance are thought stronger than those forces which keep these nurses in employment. Hence part-timers are unlikely to contain a high proportion of long-service employees, or at least are more concentrated in the extremes of short and long service. Yet in our sample part-time nurses have significantly longer periods in their current post than their full-time counterparts. Whichever average figure is consulted, part-timers record a longer time in post. Again, as few as 35 per cent have been in their current job less than a year, and as many as 25 per cent have accumulated more than five years' service; while the corresponding percentages for full-time nurses are approximately 40 per cent and just over 15 per cent. A further breakdown reveals that no group is more affected by the greater stability of the part-timers in their ranks than the generally mobile staff nurses.

The received wisdom about female and male nurses has it that while males are less prone to interrupt their career in midstream, they are more promotion conscious, and in addition those with family responsibilities are typically less restricted in geographical terms than similarly placed female colleagues. This would mean that male nurses have a longer length of employment in nursing, although the gap will be less marked where continuous service in current post is under consideration.[3] In our investigation a higher proportion of male nurses congregate at both the lowest and the highest lengths of service. For instance, 61.8 per cent of men have less than a year's service behind them in their current post, compared with 53 per cent of women. Conversely 9.2 per cent have survived more than ten years in post, while the corresponding figure for female nurses is only 2.6 per cent. Overall male nurses provide one of the highest mean length of service levels at 4.2 years, although their median and modal values are less than those of their female colleagues. The explanation lies in the particular impact of the extreme values in the higher regions among male nurses.

There is further noteworthy variation between nurses from different hospitals, although there is weak support for the predicted association between length of employment and size of hospital, or location. The main contrast centres on the proportion who have completed less than one year in their current post. At one extreme, more than one half of the trained nursing staff in two hospitals have less than a year's service, while conversely, there are four hospitals which contain fewer than 25 per cent in this category. With the significant exception of hospital J, in Table 3.1, the fluctuations are smoothed out in the upper levels of employment. Thus the convergence in the cumulative frequency distributions is well nigh achieved for those with more than ten years' employment, since only one hospital ranks much below the 90 per cent level, and even it has 80 per cent of its nurses within this range.

To summarise this brief review of the variation in completed length of service within the nursing population who responded to our first-wave questionnaire, we can point to specific categories, such as staff nurses, females, full-timers and certain hospitals which deviate noticeably below their counterparts in respect of the average stay in their current post. Similarly, these groups tend to be relatively more concentrated in the lower lengths of employment in terms of the CLS distributions. Nevertheless, the existence of such variation in nursing turnover as recorded by years in current post does not disguise a basic pattern which holds throughout the nurses considered here. At least 25 per cent of respondents from all of the subgroups have been in their present post less than a year, at least 75 per cent less than five years, and under 10 per cent have accumulated ten or more years of such continuous service. In every instance the distribution of nurses has a characteristic profile with most individuals compressed into the shorter periods.

The length of service distribution provides a further outlook on the nurses' work record when translated into an 'index of stability'. National figures permit some comparison of nurses with other occupational groups.[4] Unfortunately the computation method adopted in the *New Earnings Survey* does not correspond to the procedure followed in this study. Their rule is to include within an occupational group any trainees who are being paid a salary, but to exclude those who are on a grant. In consequence, both pupil and student nurses are located in the same category as qualified staff. The Briggs Report makes the point that this inflates the proportion of nurses with less than one year's service in comparison with, amongst others, teachers, and hence falsely creates the impression that trained nurses are less stable than is actually the case.[5] Whether nursing trainees are so manifestly more mobile than their already qualified seniors is open to some doubts, and data compiled by the General Nursing Council, as well as a small investigation by the author, demonstrate that while turnover is considerable in the first year of training, this declines rapidly and falls below the comparable level among qualified staff.[6] Notwithstanding these remarks, if we consider the *New Earnings Survey* figures for those full-time employees who have spent less than twelve months in their current post no clear trend emerges (Table 3.2). In 1973 and 1974 the administrative grades of nurse exhibited the smallest proportion with under one year in post, while nursing auxiliaries contained the highest proportion. However, in 1975 and 1976 this hierarchical effect is considerably weakened and the registered and enrolled staff become the least stable, and the gap between administrators and nursing auxiliaries is narrowed significantly. Yet even with this change all groups contain a higher proportion with twelve months' or more service in 1976 compared with 1973.

In comparison with most occupational groups, registered and enrolled nurses present a mobile front, although the behaviour of these nurses closely corresponds to that of welfare workers. The female nurses identified in Tables 3.2 and 3.3 mostly contain a lower proportion with more than a year's service than any of the non-nursing groups. While male nurses have a similar record of lower stability than their male counterparts in other occupations, their mobility has not declined in the same manner as that of other workers — whether male or female. The end product of these trends is that in the longer-service categories there is a smaller percentage of trained nurses than in the comparable category of primary school teachers, and even of clerical workers. Indeed the search for an occupational group with a worse record of instability in 1976 generates only three categories — barmaids (71.1 per cent), retail shop cashiers and check-out operators (75.2 per cent) and ship and travel clerks (80.8 per cent) — who undercut the 81 per cent figure which pertains among registered and enrolled nurses. Among others, for example, ward orderlies, waitresses, maids, assembly workers, hairdressers — all of whom are popularly regarded as highly transient workers — actually contain a larger section within their midst who have spent more than one year in their current post than is the case with trained nurses.

Since 1975 the *New Earnings Survey* has included a detailed breakdown of those with more than twelve months' service in post, and

Table 3.2: Index of Stability: Nurses and Other Selected Groups*

| | Percentage with Less than 12 Months' Service | | | | | | | |
| | 1973 | | 1974 | | 1975 | | 1976 | |
Occupation	Female	Male	Female	Male	Female	Male	Female	Male
Nurse admin.	13.4	—	15.8	—	13.8	—	11.7	6 9
Reg. and enrolled	28.4	15.8	25.6	14.4	20.0	10.5	19.0	14.0
Nurse auxiliary	29.4	—	34.2	—	18.4	—	14.3	—
Teachers (primary)	17.0	13.1	20.2	21.5	11.2	6.5	10.3	8.1
Clerical, etc.	22.5	10.8	25.3	12.9	17.4	9.5	13.4	6 4
Welfare workers	29.1	17.6	30.2	22.0	19.9	15.5	18.4	14.3
All non-manual	22.5	11.5	25.1	13.3	16.7	8.6	14.0	7.7
All occupations	22.3	14.8	24.6	15.9	16.0	10.7	13.6	9.0

*More correctly this is an instability index, since all figures are for those with less than one year in their current post.

Source: *New Earnings Survey* (HMSO, London, 1973, 1974, 1975, 1976). All figures are for full-time employees only.

figures for selected occupations on this basis are illustrated in Table 3.3. In addition, we include some comparable data from our own case study. The description of nurses as a less stable work-force is further emphasised by, for example, examining the proportion with more than five years' service, rather than that with less than a year behind them. These higher cut-off points actually produce a wider gulf between nurses and most other workers — at least in this female, full-time category. The equivalent respondents from our study are even more mobile than the national data, and contain smaller proportions with both more than one year, and more than five years' service. Part of the explanation for this may lie in the absence of nursing trainees in our figures, but there are other factors, such as our focus on District General Hospitals, which probably account for the contrasting profiles. Yet whichever data base is under observation, the stability pattern for nurses describes a predominantly short-stay group.

It also has to be borne in mind that the level of mobility in nursing described here is actually an understatement of the situation according to some reckonings. This stems from our restriction of mobility to

Table 3.3: Index of Stability: Nurses and Other Selected Groups (female, full-time staff only)

Occupation	Length of Service in Years								Percentage more than 5 years
	Under 1 year	1-2	2-3	3-4	4-5	5-9	10-14	15+	
Nursing admin.	13.8	14.8	10.8	4.3	7.0	21.3	11.1	17.1	49.3
Reg. and enrolled	20.0	22.7	16.1	10.0	6.2	13.5	6.3	5.3	25.0
Nursing auxiliaries	18.4	20.9	13.2	8.7	8.3	19.1	7.6	3.8	30.5
Teachers (primary)	11.2	21.4	11.7	8.8	8.5	20.0	8.9	9.5	38.4
Clerical, etc.	17.4	16.6	12.2	8.0	7.8	21.0	7.8	9.4	38.0
Welfare workers	19.9	20.3	14.3	10.0	7.4	16.5	6.3	5.4	28.1
All non-manual	16.7	17.3	12.1	8.2	7.7	20.2	8.2	9.7	38.0
All occupations	16.0	16.1	11.8	8.2	7.6	21.3	8.8	10.2	40.3
Our sample (full-time, women workers only)[a]									
Enrolled nurses	30.1	24.0	13.7	8.0	8.8	12.6	1.9	0.8	15.3
Staff nurse	69.5	21.3	6.6	0.4	1.5	0.7	—	—	0.7
Ward sister/ charge nurse	27.1	23.7	12.3	7.7	7.1	11.6	5.6	5.0	22.2
All	39.2	23.2	11.1	5.8	6.0	9.0	3.2	2.6	14.8

a. Proportion of nurses on 1 May 1975 with the stated length of service.
Source: *New Earnings Survey* (HMSO, London, 1975).

external movement out of an institution; and our designation of movement within an organisation's boundaries as an internal transfer, whether in terms of grade, shift, hours or ward worked. Despite this, we accept that in some cases, an internal transfer is tantamount to a departure, or a 'move without moving'. It is not so much the change in conditions which is significant but the fact that if the transfer had not been possible the nurse might well have become fully mobile and left that hospital. For example, a change in hours from full-time on the night shift to part-time during the day in order to allow a nurse to work and be at home when the children get back from school, or a change in ward to avoid a disliked colleague or work routine, are plausible alternatives to the (unwanted) trauma of resigning, and then going in search of a new post elsewhere. However, it is not appropriate to regard all internal transfers in this light. In some instances, a failure to obtain a post on another ward will not spark off a move out of the current hospital. Clearly, this is a subject which warrants in itself detailed research, and as a rough guide only, we offer a hierarchy of internal movement according to the potential threat of external mobility that arises if the transfer is blocked. At the top of the list is promotion, which is the single most potent weapon in the nurse manager's armoury to stimulate labour retention. Responses to inquiries about what might have been done to change the minds of leavers suggest that opportunities for further training are quite disproportionately distributed between hospitals and are an important factor in nurse mobility in many smaller hospitals. At some distance behind these two events, we place changes in the nurse's work conditions — whether of ward, hours or shift. If nurses are frustrated in their wish to make a move along one of these tracks, the possibility of external mobility is relatively less strong — although obviously this will be greatly affected by the range of opportunities elsewhere, and the particular circumstances of the individual nurse.[7]

The data source which we shall refer to here comprises those stayers among the original respondents who also completed the follow-up questionnaire distributed in 1976. The material contained in Table 3.4 illustrates the amount of internal transference reported for grade, hours and ward worked. The overwhelming proportion of nurses remained in the same grade over the year of our field-work, although a higher level of continuity is shown by enrolled nurses and senior ward sisters.

Table 3.4: Extent of Internal Transfer among Stayers (per cent)

Grade change

| Grade 1975 | Grade 1976 | | | | | | |
	SEN	SSEN	SN	JWS	SWS	Trainee	Admin.
SEN	93.6	5.3	—	—	—	1.1	—
SSEN	—	100.0	—	—	—	—	—
SN	—	—	76.6	17.6	2.7	3.2	—
JWS	—	—	—	79.9	17.9	0.7	1.2
SWS	—	—	—	—	93.9	4.7	1.4

N = 859

SEN = enrolled nurse; SSEN = senior enrolled nurse; SN = staff nurse;
JWS = junior ward sister; SWS = senior ward sister; Admin. = administrative grades.

A further picture of internal transfers is contained in the figures for hours, shift and ward worked. In effect full-time staff all stay on the same basis, although a section of part-timers, especially those who already work at least half-time, increase their contribution. We surmise that these nurses felt more able, or else were under more pressure in the deteriorating employment and economic climate, to work for more hours each week. Whether these nurses would have been inclined to hand in their notice if they had been refused this change is most unlikely given the then state of diminishing opportunities for employment. A change of hours parallels a movement between shifts. The significant transfer is from, or to, nights. The original group of night staff is reduced to 62 per cent, which probably reflects the inconvenience of working this shift. But lest night duty be thought universally undesirable, there is a not inconsiderable number of nurses who are attracted to work nights, especially by the extra payments received, and who might have left if a suitable vacancy had not arisen. Of all the areas of possible transfer, changes in ward are the most numerous, although by a small amount, and even here over 80 per cent of the nurses continue as they were. As a rule, the more specialised the ward, the higher the level of stability among nursing staff, but the adequate opportunities for transfer between routines may be a factor in retaining the service of some individuals.

To sum up our impression of these moves without moving, a basic continuity prevails in the nurses' routine, while there is scope for internal transfers. And these latter may depress the level of instability in some places, although its parameters are very much a question of guesswork. Even if the wholly unrealistic assumption is applied that all those who move internally would otherwise have left, the impact on the length of service distributions and turnover rates would not have been excessive. Perhaps as an approximate rule of thumb the peak of leaving might be pushed a year later and the concentration of short-service employees would be less marked, while some 5 per cent might be added to the crude separation rate. One conclusion which emerges with rather more force from this discussion is that the expected variation in internal transfers according to the size of hospitals is not confirmed. In practice, the lower level of opportunities for internal transfer in the smaller hospitals is countered by an evidently enhanced programme of promotion from within. If this is an accurate estimation of the pattern of internal hospital movement among trained nursing staff, it encourages us to think that the effect of our exclusion of such internal transfers is at least not unevenly distributed though the nursing population.

Previous Work Record

Further insights into the work record of trained nurses is gleaned from
the length of service accumulated in previous nursing jobs. As part of
the first-wave questionnaire we requested information from nurses on
the employment dates of their six most recent nursing posts. This also
enabled us to assess their continuity of employment in the NHS. In this
section we shall discuss changes in job which entailed handing in notice
to quit, together with grade changes which have not always depended
on a move to another employer or institution.

Overall, 45 per cent of respondents have not strayed from their
current hospital, whereas only 27.7 per cent are still in their first post
since qualification. If most nurses change hospital and grade at the same
time, it is evident that promotion within the same hospital is a more
frequent event than changing hospitals while continuing at the same
grade[8] (see Table 3.5). This internal grade advancement occurs most
typically in the first years of service, and is closely allied to the specific
circumstances of staff nurses. Among their more senior registered
colleagues, the longer period in the profession is reflected in the greater
number of nursing posts held and the higher number of moves between
hospitals. For example, over 60 per cent of ward sisters have had four
or more posts, while the equivalent proportion of staff nurses has
occupied no more than one post. In contrast, the gulf between the
grades in terms of the number of hospitals worked at narrows markedly.
This is not because enrolled staff noticeably move around between
hospitals, but because of the level of internal promotion reached by
registered nurses. Even the most mobile ward sisters and charge nurses
have not attained a state of perpetual motion between hospitals. Only
a quarter of ward sisters have been inside at least four hospitals. Among
other nurses, not unexpectedly, part-timers, who have usually had at
least one break from nursing, have been in relatively more hospitals
than their full-time colleagues; although there is no evident contrast
between the record of female and male nurses. A final area worthy of
mention is the apparent impact of the size of hospital where working
on mobility. The basic association is of a positive relationship between
size of hospital and number of posts held, although there is less strength
in the relationship with number of hospitals. This extension of our view
of the nurses' work record to include up to six previous jobs offers some
support for the proposition that the larger hospitals provide more
opportunities for internal promotion, although this presumes that

Table 3.5: Distribution of Nurses by Number of Posts and Number of Hospitals:
All Respondents and Selected Subgroups

	Number of Jobs/Posts (Number of Hospitals)						Mean number
	1	2	3	4	5	6	
Grade							
SEN	57.9 (64.5)	21.2 (20 7)	11.3 (10.2)	6.3 (3.6)	2.8 (0.8)	0.6 (0.3)	1.8 (1.6)
SN	39.8 (51.9)	17.3 (23 5)	16.8 (12.6)	10.4 (7.7)	6.7 (3.2)	9.1 (1.2)	2.5 (1.9)
WS/CN	– (28.6)	17.9 (27 7)	19.7 (19.5)	20.7 (14.3)	20.1 (7.1)	21.5 (2.9)	4.0 (2.5)
Hours							
FT	29.8 (46.0)	18.2 (24.0)	15.9 (14.9)	13.9 (9.2)	11.3 (4.1)	10.9 (1.8)	2.9 (2.1)
PT	17 8 (39.0)	19.3 (27.4)	19.1 (15.8)	12.9 (11 2)	12.0 (5.4)	18.7 (1.2)	3.4 (2.2)
Sex							
Female	28.3 (45.0)	17.9 (24.3)	15.7 (14.8)	13.9 (9.6)	11.1 (4.5)	13.1 (1.7)	3.0 (2.1)
Male	21.5 (42.7)	23.8 (27.5)	23.8 (16.8)	12.3 (9.2)	14.6 (2.3)	3.8 (1.5)	2.9 (2.1)
Year trained							
pre-1960	6.9 (25.0)	13.1 (25.4)	18.9 (20.8)	20.5 (17.3)	17.8 (9.2)	22.8 (2.3)	4.0 (2.7)
1960-9	10.0 (28.6)	16.2 (25.4)	16.4 (21.9)	16.9 (14.2)	17.9 (5.7)	22.6 (4.2)	3.8 (2.6)
1970-1	12.9 (38 2)	20.9 (30.7)	23.6 (16.0)	21.3 (9.8)	13.8 (4.9)	7.6 (0.4)	3.3 (2.1)
1972-3	36.4 (55.9)	30.3 (30.3)	21 1 (10.3)	8.0 (3.1)	3.4 (0.4)	0.8 (–)	2.1 (1.6)
1974-5	86.0 (88.6)	11.9 (10.6)	2.1 (0.8)	–	–	–	1.2 (1.1)
Size of hospital							
Large	23.1 (39 6)	14.7 (29.1)	18.7 (17 2)	16.1 (7.5)	14.0 (4.8)	13.4 (1.7)	3.2 (2.1)
Medium	25.6 (43.3)	20.6 (22.3)	16.4 (15 0)	12.7 (12.5)	10.8 (4.7)	13.9 (2.3)	3.0 (2.2)
Small	37 8 (54.6)	20.1 (22.1)	13.6 (12.1)	12.1 (7.4)	8.8 (2.9)	7.7 (0.9)	2.6 (1.8)
All	27.7 (44.8)	18.4 (24.6)	16.5 (15.0)	13.7 (9.6)	11.4 (4.3)	12.2 (1.7)	3.0 (2.1)

nurses remain within a certain size of hospital throughout their
working life, which is only partially borne out in our population. It is
also important that this discussion of the short time period which so
many nurses spend in individual hospitals, especially at the beginning
of their career, is set against the extra years which most have spent in
their first hospital as a trainee. In practice this extends the (mean)
average stay by two years in the case of enrolled nurses, and by three
years among registered grades (see Table 3.6).

A rather different pattern applies in respect of the mean number
of years spent in previous posts, which includes internal grade changes
and movement in and out of training courses after initial qualification.
Again part-timers are more stable than their full-time colleagues, while
males outlast female nurses, and those in smaller hospitals manage
relatively longer periods in post. There is, however, a turnaround in the
grade order when one compares average stay in posts and in hospitals.
The period for enrolled staff barely changes, which is in stark contrast
to the length of stay of registered nurses. Ward sisters are far more
prone to inherit a mixture of shorter- and longer-service positions, and
although they have a higher average stay than their junior colleagues,
the gap between them fluctuates visibly, which is primarily due to the
shorter lengths of service that ward sisters experienced as staff nurses.
This reinforces our general impression that staff nurses display the
lowest lengths of service, and that this pattern extends back for a
decade at the very least.

While there is a general tendency for nurses to dwell longest in their
later posts, there is some support for the separation of the newly
qualified between a relatively inert section and another group who
move on very quickly after qualification and who also tend to work in
several different hospitals in their early years in the profession.
Nevertheless such 'flitting' between posts and hospitals among nurses is
relatively soon overturned, and nurses as a whole settle down to a much
more stable work routine. This is especially true of full-time staff, but
rather less evident among part-time, female nurses, whose extra
instability is conditioned by their particular domestic circumstances
rather than any personality trait that inhabits this group alone.

An associated aspect of mobility between hospitals is the extent to
which nurses punctuate their career with breaks from the profession.
This may comprise leaving the NHS to undertake nursing in the private
sector, or it may involve entry into another occupation altogether. The
other significant option is to take a break from any sort of paid labour.
According to surveys commissioned by the Briggs Committee, 'a typical

Table 3.6: Mean Average Years Spent in: (i) Current Post; (ii) First
   Hospital with Any Years in Training Included; (iii) All Previous
   Posts; (iv) All Previous Hospitals

| | Mean Figure (years) | | | |
	Current Post	Current Hospital (includes training)	All Previous Posts	All Previous Hospitals
Grade				
SEN	3.4	5.1	3.2	3.8
SN	1.6	4.2	1.5	2.3
WS/CN	4.0	7.7	2.7	5.2
Hours				
FT	3.0	5.8	2.4	3.8
PT	3.7	6.8	3.0	5.1
Sex				
Female	3.0	5.9	2.4	3.8
Male	4.2	6.8	3.6	5.5
Hospital size				
Large	2.9	6.3	2.0	3.5
Medium	3.0	5.8	2.1	4.1
Small	3.5	5.7	3.1	4.5
All	3.1	6.0	2.5	4.0

"non-participating" female nurse will be a woman who is at home
looking after her family, while a typical "non-participating" male nurse
will be a man who has left nursing for some other kind of employment".[9]
The exact proportion of qualified nurses currently working in the NHS
has attracted much interest in recent years, but the best data available
are subject to a not inconsiderable margin of error. According to the
Briggs Report, the proportion of female nurses in NHS employment
drops dramatically among those now out of their early twenties or who
have been qualified no more than five years (see Table 3.7). From a
peak of 71 per cent among the under-25s, the rate declines to a plateau
around the 45 to 51 per cent level for nurses aged between 25 and 55.
These figures suggest that there is a large pool of nurses not currently in
the NHS that is alternatively enlarged by further departures from the
service, and drained by those who return to nursing. The generation of
an effective nurse manpower policy will largely hinge on this flow of
staff. It has been claimed, for example, that the 'Scottish pool' has been

Table 3.7: Participation Rates of Qualified Female Nurses and
Midwives by Age and Marital Status (Great Britain)[a]

Age	Qualified Single Female Nurses and Midwives	Qualified Married Female Nurses and Midwives[b]	All Qualified Female Nurses and Midwives
24 and under	89	53	71
25-29	84	34	45
30-39	86	39	45
40-49	78	45	51
50-59	56	46	49
60-64	24	19	25

a. Percentage number of the population defined as currently in employment in the National Health Service as a nurse or midwife.
b. Includes widowed, divorced and separated.

Source: OPCS and SCPR surveys. Taken from A. Briggs (Chairman), *Report of the Committee on Nursing* (HMSO, London, 1972), Cmnd. 7115, p. 120, Table 25.

as significant a source of recruitment as the output from training schools.[10]

The duration of these absences from nursing, and their frequency, are further areas for examination. Within our own group of respondents, 67.1 per cent of nurses currently in employment have not had a single break since they qualified, which tallies quite closely to national figures for hospital nurses.[11] Among those whose employment in the NHS was punctuated, 21.3 per cent had one break, 8.1 per cent two breaks, and a small minority of only 3.5 per cent recorded three or more gaps. The variation between the selected subgroups of nurse is in line with previous conclusions. Thus, length of time in nursing, whether represented by the date of first qualification, or the person's age, both display an unambiguous association with the number of breaks taken. The predominant characteristic of the group who have managed two or more breaks is that they qualified before 1960, and/or are more than 35 years old. In contradiction of the popular view of male staff as continuously in a specific employment, almost 20 per cent report at least one separation, which is larger than the received wisdom about the continuous service of male nurses predicts. Of course, these figures also describe what many believe is the higher propensity to return to the NHS after taking a break among female staff. At the other extreme, part-timers have almost all interrupted their careers, and this group also contains the greatest number with more than one interlude from work. Enrolled nurses have a significantly smaller number of breaks than their registered counterparts, but there is surprisingly little difference between ward sisters and staff nurses. This finding is at variance with the much more irregular work behaviour of staff nurses reported in a national survey.[12] But again we have a situation where part-timers, females and registered grades are perhaps not necessarily more prone to quit nursing, but more inclined to return after short-term breaks.

The length of any break can have an impact, because after a certain time has elapsed, individuals will be increasingly disinclined to return to the Health Service. The crucial divide looms among our nurses around three years after leaving their last nursing post. If the gap lasts much beyond that period, the umbilical cord between nurses and the NHS is ever more likely to be cut. Within those three years however, it is also unusual for individuals to take less than six months off.[13]

Again there is variation worthy of note in these figures. Full-timers, male nurses and the registered grades are congregated more in the shorter gaps from public-sector nursing, but there is no pattern which defines a 'normal' length of time in any such break.[14] Of those out of the NHS, one survey indicated that 13 per cent of nurses were in other non-NHS nursing jobs, while the remainder were split between the majority (56 per cent) who intended to return to the service, and another 29 per cent who divided between those who indicated they would never return, and others only a little less emphatic.[15] At least if nurses are a relatively mobile group with a comparatively short period in each post, especially in the early years after qualification, such behaviour does not constitute a lack of commitment to employment in the NHS.

Crude Turnover Rates

We now turn from the length of service distributions to the first of the rates of turnover included in this chapter — this is the so-called 'crude turnover rate'. The data base used consists of the material collected between May 1975 and April 1976 from official records. Our assumption that these were kept up to date proved over-optimistic in four of the fourteen hospitals, and in some cases they had to be excluded from our analysis. Unless stated otherwise, however, all of the discussion refers to the original population of nurses in post on 1 May 1975, or the respondents from that group to our first-wave questionnaire.

Separation Rate

Crude separation rates have been calculated both for the original
population and the questionnaire respondents — Tables 3.8 and 3.9
respectively. In fact, close examination of the separation rates across
the two groups indicates very few differences indeed. We have therefore
included the separation rates for the respondents in full, but have
excluded certain hospitals from Table 3.8 in order to make it directly
comparable to the crude accession rates illustrated in Table 3.10, since
those hospitals did not have the necessary information of nurse
recruitment. The so-called 'corrected' separation rate is appended to
Table 3.8 because the data base required is again restricted.

If we start with the respondents' separation rate (Table 3.9), we
calculate that it amounts to 24.9 per cent — in comparison with 24.7
per cent for nurses from every hospital in the original population. This
correspondence overall is mirrored at the individual hospital level as
well. In one instance there is a 6 per cent difference between the rates,
but in the vast majority of places the gap barely exists. Exactly the
same conclusion applies to the overall rates for the selected subgroups.
None the less, there is significant internal variation in the separation
rates. This parallels the contrasts in the completed length of service
distributions and associated averages. Thus the highest separation rate
of 38.4 per cent is among staff nurses, which considerably exceeds
the 24.2 per cent of enrolled nurses and is over twice the 16 per cent
level exhibited by ward sisters. This grade order broadly prevails
through all of the hospitals, although it is sometimes complicated by
the partial sampling of part-timers. This proved important because of
the contrast in the behaviour of part- and full-timers — especially among
staff nurses, where the difference in separation rates is at its highest
level. Nevertheless, in some hospitals the enrolled nurse rate diverges
significantly from the norm — in two instances it is very high, and in two
others extremely low. In comparison, the ward sister rate is a model of
evenness. Within these ranks, in only two hospitals does the rate exceed
20 per cent, while among staff nurses there is one solitary occasion
when it drops below 20 per cent. Overall, part-timers record higher
levels of service in post, and a lower separation rate compared to full-
time nurses: 20.7 per cent versus 25.8 per cent. The gulf between male
nurses at 15.4 per cent and female staff at 25.5 per cent is yet more
definite, and again follows the pattern illustrated in the length of
employment statistics. While caution must be shown in interpreting
the behaviour of male nurses because of the small number in this study,

Table 3.8: Crude and Corrected Separation Rates: Original Population (per cent)

Hospital	Grade			Hours		Sex		All	Corrected separation rate
	SEN	SN	WS	FT	PT	F	M		
A	29.4	29.6	13.2	21.4	a	21.6	20.0	21.4	30.5
B[b]									
C[b]									
D[b]									
E	37.5	50.0	17.2	30.5	a	26.9	57.1	30.5	37.3
F	15.4	27.3	12.0	16.1	a	15.1	22.2	16.1	25.8
G	27.6	15.8	16.0	26.3	14.3	20.8	0	20.5	26.0
H	34.6	21.3	7.1	21.4	20.2	21.2	0	20.7	23.9
I	18.5	44.4	10.8	23.4	a	24.2	17.6	23.4	32.1
J	7.4	23.1	11.4	10.8	a	11.5	6.7	10.8	11.8
K	43.8	62.1	19.4	40.2	a	40.5	33.3	40.2	49.8
L	25.3	36.8	24.8	33.5	23.2	29.7	16.7	29.1	38.2
M[b]									
N	8.0	30.8	10.2	12.6	a	12.0	25.0	12.6	18.4
All	25.3	38.4	16.3	26.5	21.1	25.8	22.1	25.5	
Corrected sep. rate	32.9	53.2	18.2	32.5	34.0	33.1	29.8		32.9

a. No part-time staff included from these hospitals.
b. Excluded because of lack of personnel data at hospital.

those present do manage the lowest level of separation among the subgroups isolated in Table 3.9.

The loss of nurses discussed this far understates the actual number of departures from those hospitals during the year under examination because our focus has been upon those in post at the beginning of our field-work. This is why we include the corrected separation rate which takes into account the leavers from among those who joined after our study commenced. The exclusion of those four hospitals which could not provide this information necessitated the adjustment in our calculations that is illustrated in Table 3.8. The result is a marginal rise in the overall separation rate to 25.5 per cent, compared with 24.7 per cent when all 14 hospitals are considered. This increase is experienced evenly through the several subgroups of nurse.

The impact of the correction to the overall separation rate is to

Table 3.9: Crude Separation Rate: Respondents to Questionnaire
(per cent)

Hospital	Grade			Hours		Sex		All
	SEN	SN	WS	FT	PT	F	M	
A	26.3	34.8	8.3	19.0	a	18.4	22.2	19.0
B	5.9	–	26.3	16.7	a	16.7	16.7	16.7
C	13.3	60.0	13.6	25.3	a	27.4	0	25.3
D	46.2	44.4	18.0	30.0	a	31.3	20.0	30.0
E	33.3	46.2	12.5	29.3	a	23.5	57.1	29.3
F	23.8	30.0	12.5	20.0	a	19.6	22.2	20.0
G	27.3	11.8	10.5	19.4	14.8	17.5	0	17.2
H	36.6	21.8	6.7	22.1	20.5	21.9	0	21.3
I	12.5	44.7	14.0	24.3	a	25.3	16.7	24.3
J	7.1	25.0	14.8	11.7	a	11.8	11.1	11.7
K	38.7	58.4	20.0	38.8	a	39.2	28.6	38.8
L	31.8	35.9	27.8	37.3	24.5	31.7	30.0	31.6
M	22.9	22.9	19.3	25.0	14.0	23.9	5.6	21.3
N	4.8	30.8	11.9	13.3	a	12.3	33.3	13.2
All	24.2	38.4	16.0	25.8	20.7	25.5	15.4	24.9

N = 1,412.
a. No part-time nurses included from this hospital.

increase the rate from 25.5 to 32.9 per cent, but the influence is differentially felt across the various groups — especially with grade and hours worked. In particular, the corrected rate catches part-timers with greater frequency, although the jump from the crude separation level varies noticeably between hospitals. The significance of this point is that it is the sole occasion when the order of the basic rate is significantly reversed. Despite the impression of greater stability which part-time nurses have demonstrated in the turnover measures up to now, the current picture is of a group of short-stay individuals within their ranks who clearly last no more than a few months before quitting. But this may contain some regularity if these part-time staff work in the same months on a 'regular' basis when the hospitals are especially short-staffed. Across the grades the other remains as before, although the gulf between them widens. Thus ward sisters, who already provide the lowest separation rate also offer the smallest corrected increase, while staff nurses who are the most mobile demonstrate the highest increase.

This further confirms the picture of staff nurses as containing a disproportionate number of short-term employees compared with other grades.

The discussion of departures within the year raises questions about its possible concentration into certain months. Suggestions of such a seasonal pattern in leaving have been mentioned in nurse staffing surveys north of the border.[16] Although we can only provide evidence from a single year's figures, this restricted viewpoint indicates several critical months when departures quicken. Part of this is due quite simply to the rapid movement of newly qualified nurses to fresh pastures, but added mobility occurs in the summer months especially. The latter has been attributed by some to those domestic pressures which oblige working mothers to look after their children during the school holidays. According to our data, which is illustrated in Figure 3.2, the early hump of departures occurs in the summer months, and gradually declines through the winter and following spring. Unfortunately the last month's figures are confused by doubts about whether the notices to quit from a handful of nurses dated from the last day of the previous month or the first day of the next month. Nevertheless, this pattern does not merge with a marked acceleration of departures when the school holidays begin nor with a fall-off as the new school year commences. The absence of the predicted trend may be due to the preponderance of young, single people in our population, but the persuasiveness of this argument is lost when a breakdown of the figures reveals a similar seasonal variation among both married women and single men. And there are few among the latter whose departure is determined by the need to look after their children. Whether different groups of reasons constrain the several groups of nurse to leave at the same time will be pursued later in our discussion of the reasons for leaving.[17]

Crude Accession Rate

The rate of recruitment is necessarily restricted to those hospitals included in Table 3.10, but the comparison with the crude separation rate for the same hospitals is slightly restricted because the data on accessions include part-time staff from every hospital. We presume that because part-timers have a longer length of employment in their current post, and since recruitment will tend to be a direct replacement, then their inclusion will depress the level of accessions. In practice, the aggregate rate of 23.5 per cent is just below the basic separation level for the same hospitals, and some 9 per cent down on the corrected

Figure 3.2: Monthly Crude Separation Rates: Original Population and
Selected Subgroups

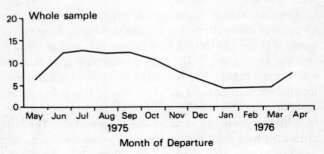

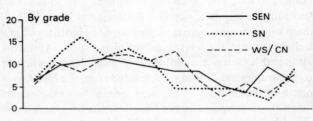

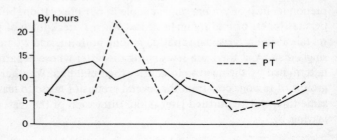

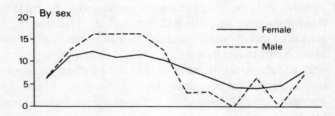

Table 3.10: Crude Accession Rate: May 1975 to April 1976 (per cent)

Hospital	Grade			Hours		Sex		All
	SEN	SN	WS	FT	PT	F	M	
A	7.5	43.8	30.8	17.6	28.7	22.6	56.3	25.6
B[a]								
C[a]								
D[a]								
E	22.5	26.7	6.5	36.4	9.7	19.6	25.0	19.8
F	5.4	25.5	31.8	32.5	6.7	15.6	64.3	20.0
G	48.3	60.0	0	52.5	14.3	34.2	50.0	34.7
H	10.7	17.2	10.8	22.5	9.0	13.9	0	13.7
I	50.0	30.6	1.8	24.8	29.3	27.7	10.0	26.9
J	3.0	16.0	0	7.2	0	5.6	0	5.1
K	15.4	30.1	4.4	18.8	16.9	18.3	0	17.8
L	34.4	55.8	14.7	38.9	28.3	35.5	17.6	34.2
M[a]								
N	19.0	36.8	21.4	12.8	35.4	23.9	33.3	24.1
All	21.5	35.3	12.9	27.0	19.4	23.3	26.2	23.5

a. No figures available.
N (starters) = 462; N (in post) = 1,969.

figure. There are other possible explanations for this discrepancy and one obvious reason is that our calculations have been in terms of people rather than hours worked. In consequence, if the nursing authorities have replaced part-time leavers with full-time recruits, at the same time as encouraging part-timers to increase the number of hours which they work (a trend which has already been noted in Table 3.4), then the relatively low accession rate is more easily understood.

Quite evidently, the aggregate accession rate of 23.5 per cent subsumes significant internal variation. The division by grade provides a now familiar order, with recruitment highest among staff nurses, followed at some distance by enrolled nurses, with ward sisters and their male counterparts bringing up the rear. Full-timers have a distinctly higher rate of recruitment than part-timers, and it is left to male nurses to provide the only unexpected feature by passing the female accession rate. As for individual hospitals, most keep close to the overall level, with the exception of Hospital J, where almost no mobility — in or out — occurred during the year of our investigation.

However, within hospitals the accession rates fluctuate wildly. The impression is that quite different recruitment policies have been followed, especially in respect of the grade and sex of nurse taken on. While recruitment is often a simple function of the range of prospective applicants, it is reasonable to suppose that nurse managers have consciously sought to organise the type of replacements. However, any trend in this direction will have been threatened by the deterioration in economic conditions and the general reduction in nursing turnover in 1976. In practice, at only two hospitals did recruitment take place at a significant level; in one, Hospital L, the high accession rate reflects the departure figures, whereas in Hospital G a policy of expansion produced the only instance where an accession rate outruns the corresponding separation level. What clues there are to a recruitment programme indicate that hospitals tend to recruit from the outside disproportionately at the junior level, and presumably rely on internal promotion and increases in hours worked to bring their staff resources back to an equilibrium position.

Case Study of Crude Turnover Rates, 1971-1975

Several references have been made to the fluctuation in turnover in recent years, in response, most argue, to the changing unemployment situation. We have demonstrated that the monthly rate of departures declined between 1975 and 1976, but in this section we present information stretching back through the early 1970s that was made available by one of the large teaching hospitals in our sample.[18]

In broad outline, the pattern of departures from this hospital during the period 1971 to 1975 approximates to what is generally believed to have happened. The crude separation level for 1975 is lower than anything else recorded from the previous years (and has declined further since 1975). The peak of separations during this period was 1973, so that departures both increased and then declined significantly over these five years. Within this rate there is considerable variation according to the grade of the nurse. Again the order of staff nurse, enrolled nurse, ward sister in descending propensity to leave is clearly illustrated in every year considered. In broad terms the staff nurse separation rate is around three times that of ward sisters, and usually twice as large as the enrolled nurse proportion. The sole exception occurs in 1975 when the decline in the separation rate of registered staff is not matched by a parallel decrease among enrolled nurses. The dominant effect on nursing turnover is always attributable therefore to the staff nurse group, since not only are they a significant group within nursing in

Table 3.11: Crude Separation Rate, 1971-1975: Single Hospital Figures (per cent)

Year	Grade				Percentage Unemployed[a]	
	SEN	SN	WS/CN	All	UK	Yorks.
1971	31.5	57.1	18.9	42.3	3.4	4.0
1972	32.9	71.5	16.5	47.9	3.7	4.1
1973	37.5	74.7	18.0	50.8	2.6	2.8
1974	34.6	64.4	22.5	44.6	2.6	2.6
1975	37.3	51.0	8.7	36.7	3.9	3.8

a. Source: Department of Employment returns.

terms of numbers but their rate is always the most responsive to change.

Data on the accession rate at the same hospital confirms the distinctive pattern of nursing turnover during this period. Recruitment at first rises, and then drops to its lowest level by far in 1975, although it does lag behind the separation rate by several months. While the accession rate in each grade is lower in 1975 than in any other year, the grades do not move uniformly. This confusion is most evident in the registered grades, since the enrolled nurses stay within a relatively narrow band for both accession and separations. If a policy on recruitment is in operation it does not come through in these figures, or it has not been pursued consistently from one year to the next.

The inclusion of national and regional unemployment rates in Table 3.11 permits us to trace the association between trained nurse mobility and wider economic conditions. While there is the predicted relationship so that separation levels are greatest when unemployment is low, the correlations of -0.3 with the national rate and -0.2 with the regional unemployment level are by no means as large as has been reported for other workers, usually in manufacturing industry.[19] As a professional group, trained nurses are perhaps more insulated from wider employment circumstances than manual workers, but calculations which we have made for a small group of nursing auxiliaries indicate that the relationship between their crude separation rate and national unemployment levels is barely different from that exhibited by their trained colleagues.

To conclude this examination of the crude turnover rates, we have reported further support for the view that trained nurses display a noteworthy level of movement, but that there is much variation within their ranks. The next step is to resolve the question whether the lack of control for length of service has significantly affected this pattern, and therefore we pursue this discussion of nursing turnover by looking at cohort rates.

Cohort Turnover Rates

The two cohort rates discussed here are the survival (or retention) rate, and the wastage (or departure) rate. Such rates obviously bypass the level of recruitment except in so far as cohorts vary in size, or 'fill up' at different speeds. Our data base in this section is the reduced group of hospitals, with entrants placed in four cohorts from the beginning of 1975 to the first four months of 1976. In each cohort there are approximately the same number of nurses, and equally there is a close correspondence in the distribution of recruits according to grade, hours worked and sex of nurse. All of the groups are traced through until August 1976 so that the first entrants will have accumulated up to eighteen months' service if they did not leave.

The stability rate for the first cohort is 62.3 per cent and this increases steadily through 68.2 per cent for the second to 79.6 per cent for the third cohort. More unexpectedly, the survival rate for the recruits in 1976 holds at exactly the same level as in the previous cohort. The presumption that those who are least 'at risk' of leaving will display the highest stability is therefore rejected in the most recent entrants. One explanation is that the early peak of leaving occurs in the first six months of employment and then diminishes to a trickle, but even if this is true the extra months of employment available to the third cohort and the decline in turnover revealed in the separation rates should have ensured some difference between them. An alternative interpretation is based on the resurrection of the seasonal pattern in departures. Stability is not then a simple function of time spent in post, but is determined by the more complex interaction between length of service and time of the year when the person joined the organisation. The existence of the same wastage rate in the two most recent cohorts is then explained in part by the bigger losses during the summer months which nullify the slightly higher possibility of departure that one attributes to the earlier cohort's members.

Otherwise, the pattern of leaving implies that pressures occur at fairly regular time intervals, which make movement more desirable or feasible. There is the anticipated early peak — between three and six months — followed by a moderate, albeit steady decline, but there is a resurgence of itchy feet after about a year in post. If we consider the

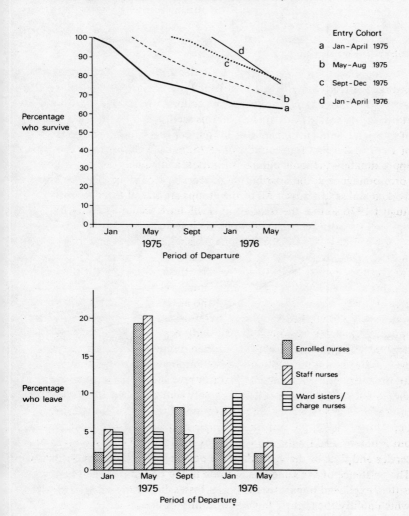

Figure 3.3: Cohort Turnover Rates: (i) Overall Survival Rates;
(ii) Wastage Rates by Grade, First Cohort Only

Entry Cohort

a   Jan – April 1975

b   May – Aug 1975

c   Sept – Dec 1975

d   Jan – April 1976

Percentage
who survive

Period of Departure

Enrolled nurses

Staff nurses

Ward sisters /
charge nurses

Percentage
who leave

Period of Departure

Figure 3.4: (i) Wastage Rate Distribution: All Entrants, 1975;
(ii) Survivor Curve, by Cohort, 1975

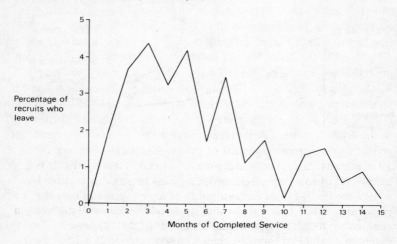

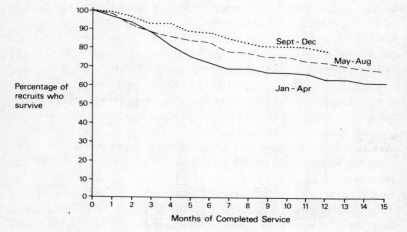

first cohort only and examine those in more detail, approximately three-fifths of all leavers over the eighteen-month interval quit within their first eight months in employment. Afterwards the wastage rate is much reduced. This applies to all nursing recruits, except ward sisters (see Figure 3.3). Yet even with this general decrease there are notable differences in the actual level of mobility. The three grades display the now 'normal' order, so that staff nurses have the lowest survival rate, ward sisters the highest, and enrolled nurses are in the middle of this registered nurse sandwich. Nevertheless, the gap between the grades is not as high as already illustrated in the length of service distributions, or the crude turnover rates. Indeed the trend stirring in the most recent cohort suggests a rearrangement of the usual hierarchy. Among the 1976 recruits staff nurse wastage declines so considerably that it falls below that of enrolled nurses, which remains remarkably steady. This echoes the finding from our case study of separation rates over the period since 1971 that it is the staff nurse rate which oscillates most in comparison to the far less volatile behaviour of their colleagues. To an extent not exhibited by other grades, staff nurses are closely attuned to the changing employment situation in general, and to the reduction of nursing vacancies and decreasing promotion prospects in particular. Ward sisters and charge nurses stand apart because their crest of leaving occurs only after a year in post, and in contrast to other nurses the early months are apparently less of a hurdle.

As with other measures, part-timers have a higher survival rate than their colleagues, and their rate holds more or less constant relative to the massive decline in the full-time rate. Hence the characteristic early pinnacle is less evident among part-timers. These features suggest that their reasons for departure are rather less conditioned by recent constraints within the Health Service than is the case with their full-time colleagues.

A yet more precise illustration of the time basis in wastage rates among the cohorts of new entrants appears in Figure 3.4. The survivor function curve across the cohorts is strikingly similar, while both graphs specify an early exodus during the first half-year of employment, with a weakened resurgence after a year's service.

Force of Separation

Questions about the time basis of leaving lead easily into the analysis of the force of separation among nurses. This is calculated both for the cross-sectional data provided by our questionnaire respondents, and the cohort material. In both, the aim is to derive a transition probability —

which in this discussion comprises the propensity to leave a particular hospital post.

Statistics for the force of separation are represented diagrammatically in Figure 3.5. These demonstrate the manner in which the probability of leaving rises and falls with length of service. The general pattern of ebb and flow applies to all nurses, and is maintained after a breakdown of the groups by grade, hours worked and sex. However, while the peaks and troughs exist in all sections of the nursing community, the point at which these occur, and their intensity, vary significantly. Indeed we detect what have hitherto been hidden elements in nursing turnover. Up to the present, the powerful association between length of service and leaving has been emphasised, while allowance is made for internal variation. Now we have information which contradicts the assumption of a straightforward linear relationship. Among our respondents, the cross-sectional data illustrated in Figure 3.5 indicate that the propensity to leave shifts over time. The likelihood of quitting is most acute in the early years of service, but it decreases almost as sharply after the first year in post to a low point between three and four years' completed service. After this point the transition probability increases again to something of a plateau between seven and twelve years in post. A final turn-about occurs among those with the longest employment lengths. The whole structure is comparable to a 'roller-coaster'. In that earlier discussion of cohort turnover rates it transpired that the several categories of nurse displayed the same accelerated early leaving, although their subsequent behaviour bore fewer resemblances. The force of separation statistics locate this early peak between three and seven months into a new post, after which stage the trend is clearly for enhanced stability. Thus while the actual propensity to leave varies in absolute terms, several common features exist between nurses. This conclusion reinforces the picture revealed in our discussion of the length of service figures, as well as the turnover rates. Yet the force of separation probabilities indicate that these other measures have not grasped the tendency in the upper levels of service for the grade hierarchy in leaving to be overturned. Between three and nine years in post, the likelihood of departure across the grades narrows considerably from the 'normal' order. After about ten years in post, the staff nurse representation has been lost, after a progressive diminution in their leaving rate. In complete contrast, the enrolled nurses quickly recover from their early mobility peak, and the force of separation in their case rises with increasing intensity. Indeed, the propensity to quit is higher in the upper service levels than at any

Figure 3.5: Force of Separation: (i) Questionnaire Respondents, by Grade; (ii) Questionnaire Respondents; (iii) All Entrants, 1975

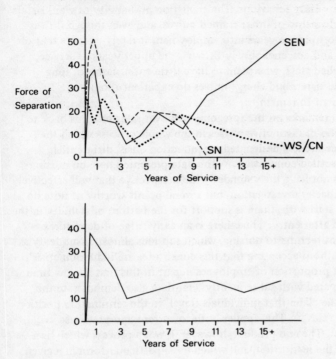

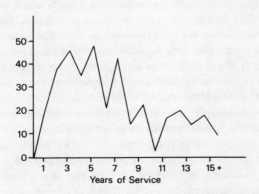

Scale : 100 equals all left

other time, and is also much in excess of their colleagues' rate. In both of the registered grades the readiness to leave in the early years is never challenged by later behaviour. The transition probability of ward sisters is always below that of other trained nurses, and even though it rises between five and nine years into employment it rarely exceeds that of other staff, and descends slowly through the upper years of service. Unlike enrolled staff, who seem to have little enthusiasm for long service, ward sisters and charge nurses do experience some encouragement to remain.

Our final remarks on the foregoing turnover rates bring us back to the prediction of distinctive phases in the whole process which the Tavistock researchers designated as: induction crisis, differential transit and settled connection.[20] The data presented here on nursing turnover do not have the extended time perspective that will effectively match the Glacier investigation, but several points worthy of note do emerge. To start with, there is support for the pattern of stability in the early period after entry. Thus there is an early surge of departures among recent recruits to nursing, which subsides almost as suddenly as it begins. Without accepting that this constitutes an 'induction crisis', a significant proportion of employees depart in this first narrow time period compared with subsequently. Our data also demonstrate the validity of the claim that individuals travel 'to the termination position at different rates'.[21] This applies both to current and previous employment. The end product, however, is not a process which 'is a function of the institution, and which has a particular form in a given factory',[22] but one that is ordered by the particular work relations within hospitals and additionally by outside constraints which pressure individuals according to their own circumstances as well as wider conditions to stay or leave. We have reported on variation in turnover between nurses according to their grade, hours worked and sex, which basically holds firm in a certain order throughout the several measures discussed here. Yet the reasons that a high proportion of staff nurses compared to ward sisters leave in their early months of employment are explained not by the individuals who comprise these groups, as the Tavistock team imply, but by a much more complex interaction between job features and social conditions. To claim otherwise is to propose that individuals with different personalities occupy the different grades, that some types work full-time and others part-time, and that males are so different to women. The fact of nursing is of course that the same individuals move between several of these categories, at least between the grades, and number of hours worked.

It is not that some are pre-ordained as more marginal to those employing them, whatever the hospital and stage in their career or life, but that the constraints on nurses in work fluctuate, and are transformed. This view is reinforced by the information on previous work behaviour. Those who moved quite often in their early days have become far more settled with time, and it seems reasonable to presume that many of the current crop of short-service employees will establish a similar connection later in their nursing life.

One way of saving the Tavistock model is to adapt it slightly to the rather peculiar conditions of NHS employment of nurses. Therefore the connection that nurses build up is not so much with a particular hospital, but rather with the profession itself, or with the NHS. The early peak of leaving consists of both those who have suffered some unfortunate experience or for some other reason found themselves in the wrong place, as well as others who might more properly be thought 'perpetually' in a state of differential transit. That is, they have survived the early introduction into nursing as a trainee, but they have decided to move on quickly to another hospital in order to see what their prospects are as a fully qualified nurse. This warrants a union of departure rates for individual hospitals with overall participation rates among nurses. A distinction must be drawn between labour turnover as a social process which takes people away from an individual institution as well as one which takes them out of nursing entirely.

The Direction of Nursing Turnover

Statements about the level of labour turnover invariably omit any details about the direction in which the individuals have moved. Yet for those given the responsibility for rectifying and controlling labour instability, as well as for those with a more academic interest, the understanding of its genesis and scope will be extremely partial unless answers are provided to such questions as: do the leavers continue in nursing, and if so, do they remain in the NHS? Do they renounce paid employment altogether, perhaps prematurely, perhaps temporarily? To what degree are the leavers geographically mobile? The importance of these issues is brought home when one remembers that the responses taken by nurse managers and social scientists alike depend on whether the mobility of nursing staff is contained within the service or if it produces a heavy exodus out of the NHS. For all those struggling to understand nursing turnover, a full explanation must take into account the direction taken on leaving the current post, and why that rather than one of several alternatives is chosen; or conversely, why individuals

Figure 3.6: Direction of Turnover: Original Population Leavers

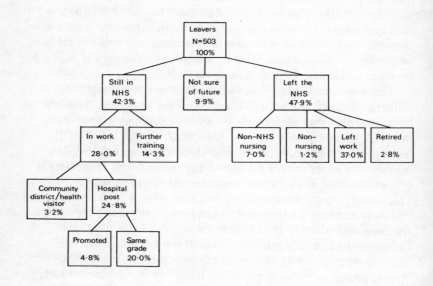

have remained in their current post. We shall reserve comment on the circumstances which trigger mobility along one avenue rather than another until the next chapter. In this section we concentrate on the extent of mobility in the different directions, and its variation within the nursing population.

We have already mentioned that the flow of labour mobility can take a variety of forms: in Figure 3.6 is the final list of destinations within which we grouped our nurses. The initial breakdown separates those who stay in the NHS from the remainder who quit the service. This is supplemented by a secondary division; in the case of those who leave the NHS we indicate more specifically whether the move is to another job, and if so, whether as a nurse or not. If the individual continues in the NHS we examine what proportion go to another hospital, as well as how many enter some form of non-hospital nursing. The other category of stayers comprises those who are taking a course of further training. A final splitting of those who take another NHS post distinguishes between those promoted and those who continue at the same grade level.

The overall pattern of leaving is supplemented in Table 3.12 by a further breakdown according to the grade, hours worked and sex of nurse. These figures indicate that almost one-half of all leavers slot into one of the four categories which encompass a clean break with the service. There are reasons to suppose that the true figure is nearer to 60 per cent, since a majority of those unable to spell out their future plans, or for whom no information was available, are on the point of leaving the NHS but are reluctant to spell out the reason for their impending defection. Of the departees from the service, by far the greater number are on their way out of work entirely. These nurses are subdivided into a relatively small group (2.8 per cent) who report that they have attained the retirement age, and a much larger body (37.0 per cent) who are either stopping work prematurely or temporarily. There are relatively few who take another post outside the NHS, whether as nurses (7.0 per cent) or in some other occupation (1.2 per cent). The group which includes those now nursing outside the NHS actually covers both those who have taken a post in the private sector or agency nursing in Britain, as well as what proved to be a larger number who leave Britain, mainly to return to their home country, and who carry on nursing. But for most of the nursing population, the alternatives are clear-cut: either continue as a nurse in the NHS or give up work entirely. No more than one in ten nurses opts for non-NHS

Table 3.12: Direction of Turnover: Original Population, by Grade, Hours and Sex of Nurse (per cent)

| | Grade | | | Hours | | Sex | | All |
	SEN	SN	WS/CN	FT	PT	F	M	
Move to another NHS post	28.2	27.5	28.0	28.6	23.8	26.9	41.9	28.0
Further training	6.9	25.3	3.5	16.3	3.8	14.0	19.4	14.3
Not sure (of future)	14.5	7.4	9.8	11.1	10.0	9.3	19.4	9.9
Non-NHS nursing	6.1	7.9	6.3	7.8	2.5	7.4	—	7.0
Other work	2.3	1.3	—	1.2	1.3	1.1	3.3	1.2
Left work (early)	33.6	30.6	50.3	33.1	57.5	39.0	6.5	37.0
Retired	8.4	—	2.1	3.1	1.3	2.3	9.7	2.8
								100

nursing, or a new occupation. Furthermore, some two-thirds of those handing in their notice envisage a future where they will return to NHS nursing, and this figure parallels the findings of the Briggs Report.[23] While one is entitled to misgivings about the reliability of such predictors about future behaviour, they further supplement an attachment among trained nurses to NHS employment (however much this is constrained by the lack of alternative opportunities) that defies contradiction.

That premature withdrawal from work so outruns age-determined retirement reminds us of the preponderance of younger nurses in this population. Nevertheless there are some indications that female nurses operate with their own notion of the 'proper' retirement age, and several still in their 40s and 50s offer this as the main reason for their departure — which if nothing else reinforces their intention to quit. Of those who remain in the NHS but who transfer to another nursing post (42.1 per cent), the vast majority move to another hospital (24.8 per cent), while 3.2 per cent leave the hospital environment for a community/district/health visitor post. Promotion is widely accepted as a primary influence on those who simply go from one hospital to another, although other possible incentives include an improvement, or change, in hours, shift, colleagues, specialism and so forth. In fact, promotion is a primary factor with no more than a minority of these leavers. Few enrolled nurses enjoy prospects of advancement anyway but registered staff as well are inclined to move to another institution without changing their grade. This horizontal mobility is however more characteristic of ward sisters than staff nurses. Those who stay in the NHS also include a noteworthy minority who embark on a course of further training. With few exceptions the option favoured is a midwifery qualification. To designate this group as stayers is perhaps premature, if formally correct, since for some this is a half-way house before cutting either the NHS, or nursing link, or both. The additional qualification is often regarded as an insurance policy, 'just in case'.

The pattern of mobility outlined above affords some immediate contrasts with the directions chosen by other workers. To start with, there is the very high proportion of nurses who leave work altogether. This is a phenomenon typically associated with a predominantly female work-force which is expected to give up employment outside the home when the responsibilities of the latter become too onerous, or simply come into conflict. For those who remain in work, the overwhelming impression is of a high degree of occupational stability. There is no well trodden route out of nursing to another area of employment. Not only do few change their occupation, but there is scarcely any transfer out of the public sector into private nursing. And few change their employer, unless one interprets this as a move to another Area Health Authority. The obvious reluctance to quit the NHS reflects its monopsony position; not unexpectedly, when another occupation is chosen, the transfer from nursing work is usually minimal. It centres in the main on those areas where nursing knowledge and experience are of immediate use — such as doctor's receptionist, housekeeper and so forth.[24]

Within these broad outlines, there is scope for variation according to the nurse's background. We have already reported that staff nurses are over-represented among leavers, and these figures on direction indicate further specificities in their behaviour. Alone of the three grades, the majority in this group stay in NHS nursing. This no doubt reflects their heightened facilities for inter-hospital moves, as well as the lower constraints on mobility among young, single persons. In comparison, enrolled nurses and ward sisters also contain about 28 per cent of their number who stay in the NHS, but neither of these groups throws up the same number who are undertaking further training. Among those who quit the service entirely, ward sisters are particularly prominent, while enrolled nurses are relatively more likely to claim retirement as their avenue out of the NHS.

In other areas, 45 per cent of full-timers are continuing in the NHS compared with 27.6 per cent of part-time nurses. Not only do more full-time staff leave in order to undertake a course of further training, but more transfer directly to another hospital post. At the same time, it is the full-timers who constitute the main force to non-NHS nursing. This leaves the heaviest concentration of part-time staff among those giving up work altogether. Yet the contrast between the grades, and between full- and part-time workers, is nothing like as sharp as the differences evident between male and female staff. Among males, 61.3 per cent stay in the service, which far exceeds the 40.9 per cent figure for females, and this contains a surplus of both those taking another hospital post as well as those going into further training. Furthermore, within that group of male nurses who quit the service, most are compelled to depart because they have attained the retirement age, or because of sickness. Interestingly, all those who take up nursing outside the NHS are females.

The current mobility of those from our population who left during the year of our field-work can also be set against the previous directional changes reported by our respondents. Clearly, we are considering a very particular group who have either never left the NHS or who have returned after some such break(s). Of those who have taken a break from nursing since qualification, 46.7 per cent say that they continued in work, but three-quarters of this contingent simply moved from public to private nursing. Indeed a fair proportion who enter private agency nursing find themselves sent back to NHS hospitals, although on a more flexible part-time basis than they were used to previously. The only other category worthy of note encompasses personal service employment. The SCPR study shows that approximately one-quarter of nurses have worked in a nursing post outside the NHS, which is higher than the 15 per cent contained in our respondents. There is agreement, however, that the largest group who have had a gap in their NHS career have taken a break from all paid labour. As a rule they have had to look after their families full-time instead.

While greater knowledge about those qualified nurses who are currently outside the NHS is really necessary to draw firm conclusions about the direction of labour turnover among trained nurses, the definite impression from this brief view of prior changes is that nursing enjoys a firm loyalty from its trained staff. That is to say, once nurses have entered the profession there is a high level of attachment, which usually means that they either do not stray far or, more often, do not take up any other paid employment whatsoever.

Table 3.13: Occupational Direction during Break from Nursing (per cent)

	Sex		Grade		All[a]
	Female	Male	Enrolled	Registered	
Other nursing	31.8	29.2	22.7	33.6	31.6
Other non-manual	9.7	50.0	31.8	8.0	12.7
Skilled manual	0.3	8.3	—	1.0	0.8
Semi- and unskilled manual	1.5	8.3	6.0	1.0	1.6
Gave up working	56.8	4.2	39.4	56.4	53.4

a. N = 364.

Geographical Mobility

Whatever their level of mobility, it has been widely accepted that nurses have a predilection for moving relatively greater distances than is usual in the population at large.[25] This geographical mobility is encouraged by the widely dispersed opportunities throughout the country for nurses, although the attraction of a new post may stem from non-nursing factors related to the area in which the hospital is located. This facet of labour turnover has obvious practical import to the nursing authorities in the construction of long-term manpower plans. Most forecasts argue that|the more skilled grades will be recruited across the greatest distances. In nursing this means|that nursing auxiliaries are drawn almost exclusively from the district in which the hospital is situated, while the net for registered staff has a regional or even national basis. Enrolled nurses fit in between these extremes. What nurse planners will want to know is how far their region experiences a net outflow or inflow of staff.[26] But just as factors within nursing are a significant influence on geographical, as other, mobility, so too there are many domestic and social circumstances which will|have a part to play. In general these influences will interact so that the early changes after qualification — when people are younger, with fewer domestic commitments, and there are more opportunities for further training and promotion — will not only be more frequent but will entail travel over the greater distances. With the passage of time this mobility will subside and contract.

Information on geographical mobility among nurses is illustrated in Table 3.14. This|highlights the crucial extent of mobility between place of training and present employment. Quite evidently, there is very little in this instance; the majority of nurses are working in the same district as the one in which they first qualified, and for most of these there has been no movement out of their first hospital. Another 28.8 per cent have merely transferred around within the region, so this amounts to over 80 per cent of the respondents who have retained their county location, although a small minority have actually moved out and then back again in the interim between training and their current post in Yorkshire. Of the remainder some 18.9 per cent trained elsewhere in the United Kingdom, and a lone 1.2 per cent qualified abroad. The British migrants into the county generally did not travel long distances but typically crossed over the immediate borders. Some 37.8 per cent originate in the surrounding counties — Northumberland and Cumbria to the north, Cheshire and Lancashire to the west,

Table 3.14: Relationship between Present Hospital and Location of
Place where Trained (per cent)

Place where trained	Present Hospital									
	A	B	C	D	E	F	G	H	I	All[a]
Same as present hospital	23.3	50.2	64.6	55.6	61.4	51.1	46.3	53.2	59.2	52.4
Elsewhere in West Yorkshire	38.2	25.2	15.6	16.6	21.6	13.0	21.5	28.0	21.0	22.4
Other Yorkshire	10.0	6.4	3.1	5.1	3.3	2.2	7.8	0.8	7.9	5.1
Other UK	27.5	17.2	16.7	11.6	11.4	30.8	22.9	18.3	11.8	18.9
Abroad	0.8	1.0	—	1.0	2.2	2.7	1.5	—	—	1.2

a. N = 1,390.

Nottinghamshire, Lincoln and Derbyshire to the south. Another 14.4
per cent came from the Midlands and East Anglia, and the diminution
in recruits with distance is only reversed by a sizeable group (26.4 per
cent) from the south of the country — with 18.2 per cent from the
Greater London area alone. The representation of nurses from other
constituent countries within the UK is relatively small; Scotland
provides 8.6 per cent, Wales 2.1 per cent and Northern Ireland's total
is a mere 0.7 per cent. Of those who trained abroad, the majority
originate in one of the Commonwealth countries, and a few come from
Europe.

Again variation within this overall pattern can be illustrated. For
example, enrolled nurses remain closer to their place of training than
registered staff. Indeed the more senior ward sisters and charge nurses
reveal the smallest contingent from Yorkshire, although even then as
many as two-thirds of this group have not left their original district.
Nevertheless, almost one-quarter of ward sisters have arrived from
outside the county compared with 15.6 per cent of staff nurses and
12.7 per cent of enrolled nurses. Although the gap between male and
female staff is not large, rather more of the former trained outside the
county, while a similar conclusion applies in the case of full-timers.

The introduction of controls for the number of previous posts held
indicates that the distance from place where the nurse qualified
becomes progressively greater as the breadth of experience is increased.

Over 95 per cent of those in their first post after qualification also trained within the county, and Table 3.15 demonstrates that the early movement between posts is similarly contained. It is not until one reaches those with at least five posts to their name that more than half of the nurses resided outside Yorkshire. Given that relatively few nurses have attained this level of turnover, it is reasonable to presume that geographical mobility is more the rule than the exception. It is notable none the less that the distance outwith Yorkshire increases apace with the range of hospital and post experience. The proportion from the North and Midlands advances from 10.9 to 27.8 per cent for posts, and from 12.0 to 33.3 per cent for hospitals, and comparable increases appear among those from London and the South of England, elsewhere in the UK, and in those from abroad.

The information contained in Table 3.16 re-emphasises the extent to which individual mobility is restrained within relatively narrow boundaries. The message is that when each move made by nurses between posts is considered, an absolute majority is contained within Yorkshire, but of those who enter the county the majority migrate from no further than the North and Midlands. And while there has been some toing and froing between Yorkshire and the rest of the areas over time, there is a more typical pattern whereby those who travel from far afield make one large jump, rather than several little ones.

A breakdown by grade and sex indicates that males are the least geographically mobile by far — indeed they are an exclusively Northern (plus a few Midland) based group, in terms of their work experience in nursing. Although registered nurses are the more cosmopolitan category

Table 3.15: Geographical Location of Previous Post(s) (per cent)

Previous Post Numbers[a]	Same district	Other Yorks.	North and Midlands	London and South	Other UK	Abroad	N[b]
2	45.4	34.3	10.9	6.0	2.5	0.8	996
3	31.2	38.6	16.9	8.4	2.4	2.6	741
4	23.1	34.9	23.1	12.4	5.6	3.1	517
5	21.6	26.9	27.8	12.7	6.5	4.6	324
6	14.0	32.0	27.8	15.4	9.5	2.4	169

a. Post 2, 3 and so on refers to the second most recent post, third most recent, etc.
b. No information/not applicable excluded.

Table 3.16: Geographical Mobility for Each Change of Hospital Post (per cent)

Post 1	Yorkshire	North and Midlands	London and South	Other UK	Abroad	N	Percentage
			Post 2				
Yorkshire	79.7	10.9	6.0	2.5	0.8	996	100.0
Post 2			Post 3				
Yorkshire	80.2	11.5	4.7	1.5	2.2	592	80.3
North and Midlands	25.6	60.3	10.3	2.6	1.3	78	10.6
London and South	25.6	9.3	53.5	4.7	7.0	43	5.3
Other UK	23.5	29.4	5.9	35.3	5.9	17	2.3
Abroad	57.1	—	28.6	—	14.3	7	0.9
All	69.7	16.8	8.4	2.4	2.6	737	100.0
Post 3			Post 4				
Yorkshire	76.1	12.7	6.0	3.0	2.1	331	65.0
North and Midlands	22.7	59.8	10.3	5.2	2.1	97	19.1
London and South	17.6	15.7	56.9	7.8	2.0	51	10.0
Other UK	7.7	15.4	15.4	61.5	—	13	2.6
Abroad	35.3	11.8	5.9	11.8	35.3	17	3.3
All	57.0	22.0	12.2	5.7	3.1	509	100.0

because of their representation in the remoter parts of the UK, and abroad generally, they also contain a similar number who have restricted their geographical horizons to one county as enrolled nurses. If the latter move more frequently from outside of Yorkshire in the specific case of the transfer to their present post, they have no extended record of geographical mobility. Furthermore, they rarely travel long distances to change jobs. Among our enrolled nurse respondents, the number who originate more than 150 miles beyond the county boundaries may be counted on the fingers of one hand. This pattern of geographical mobility among trained nurses mirrors the movement of people in the general population.[27] Typically, the more highly qualified the individual, the more prepared they are to exhibit much wider mobility, but even so the proportion of such movers remains below 20 per cent of the total work-force.

Summary

This picture of trained nurses represents them as an essentially short-service group, who are highly mobile in the early years after qualification, but within the service. Something like one-quarter of nurses 'turnover' each year, but few of these move more than once within that period. As a rule the propensity to depart exhibits a notable peak in the first six months after starting a new job; then it declines, although in some groups the probability of leaving increases once again in the higher lengths of service. Nurse mobility invariably entails either a movement to another hospital or a transfer out of work altogether. Those who leave (and later return) and take up another post usually opt for some type of private nursing. Approximately one-third of those currently in post have strayed, or originated, outside the region, but there is little inclination to be mobile over long distances. In sum, the mobility of trained nurses assumes a distinguishable profile: little is across occupations or between employers (i.e. beyond the NHS), and mobility between regions is only moderately evident. Instead, nurse turnover is essentially 'inter-firm' or 'in and out of work'. Within these broad outlines many instances of internal variation have been illustrated, but these do not overturn the general conclusions. What remains is to examine the conditions under which the nursing turnover described here occurs.

Notes

1. A. Briggs (Chairman), *Report of the Committee on Nursing* (HMSO, London, 1972), Cmnd. 7115; J. MacGuire, *Threshold to Nursing*, Occasional Papers on Social Administration, no.30 (Bell, London, 1969); S. Redfern, 'Absence and Wastage in Trained Nurses: A Selective Review of the Literature , *Journal of Advanced Nursing*, vol.3 (1978), pp.231-49.
2. A. Sims, P. Long and M. Saunders, 'The Trained Nurse in England and Wales', unpublished report, General Nursing Council, London, 1977; P.M. Abel, P. Farmer, M. Hunter and P. Shipp, 'Nursing Manpower: a Sound Statistical Base for Policy Making', *Nursing Times*, Occasional Papers 5-8 (January 1976); L. Hockey, *Women in Nursing* (Hodder and Stoughton, London, 1976); J. Morton-Williams and R. Berthoud, 'Nurses Attitude Survey', unpublished report on Personal Interview Survey, Social and Community Planning Research (SCPR), London, 1971 (henceforth referred to as 'Nurse Interview Survey); J. Morton-Williams and R. Berthoud, 'Nurses Attitude Survey', unpublished report on Postal Survey, Social and Community Planning Research, London, 1971 (henceforth referred to as 'Nurse Postal Survey').
3. Morton-Williams and Berthoud, 'Nurse Postal Survey', pp.84-7.
4. *New Earnings Survey, 1975* (HMSO, London, 1976); DHSS, 'Leavers:

Standard Measures and Classifications' (Maplin Report no.1) (DHSS, London 1975). See also footnote 20, Chapter 2.

5. Briggs, *Report of the Committee on Nursing*, pp.123-4; J. Harris, *Nurse Wastage Study* (DHSS, London, 1974); Scottish Home and Health Department. 'The Movements of Hospital Nursing Staff in Scotland', Nursing Manpower Planning Report no.5 (SHHD, 1975).

6. The General Nursing Council for England and Wales, *Annual Report, 1976-77* (GNC, London, 1978); G. Mercer, 'Fluctuations over Time in the Rate of Nursing Turnover', unpublished report, University of Leeds, 1978.

7. G. Mercer, C. Mould and L. Taggart, 'Nurses on the Move', *Nursing Times*, no.72 (1976), pp.441-3.

8. Morton-Williams and Berthoud, 'Nurse Postal Survey', pp.84-7.

9. J. Sadler and T. Whitworth, *Reserves of Nurses* (HMSO, London, 1975). p.7.

10. G. Lind, J. Luckman and C. Wiseman, *Qualified Nurses Outwith the Scottish NHS* (Tavistock Institute of Human Relations, 1977).

11. Morton-Williams and Berthoud, 'Nurse Postal Survey', pp.90-102.

12. Ibid., p.99.

13. Ibid., pp.98-102. Indeed it seemed to us that a break was not a break unless at least six months was spent away from work. Many people including nurses, who have taken another job do not take up the new employment immediately, but to interpret short interludes while sorting out moves to another hospital as a 'break from work' seems overly formalistic. For a contrary viewpoint see Lind *et al.*, *Qualified Nurses Outwith the Scottish NHS.* They report that 72 per cent of whole-time enrolled nurses, 83 per cent of whole-time registered, 25 per cent of part-time enrolled and 19 per cent of part-time registered take a break of less than six months – usually no more than a week or two between posts.

14. Morton-Williams and Berthoud, 'Nurse Postal Survey', pp.98-102.

15. Reported in: G. Lind *et al.*, *Qualified Nurses Outwith the Scottish NHS*, pp.8-9.

16. Scottish Home and Health Department, *Practical Manpower Planning for Nurses*, Report no.2 (SHHD, Edinburgh, 1974), pp.31-9.

17. The crude separation rates have been calculated for our respondents and weighted to allow for the number of worker hours, rather than bodies, lost. The weighted rate is given first, and the Table 3.10 figures are included for comparison in brackets. SEN 24.1% (24.2); staff nurse 41.2% (38.4); ward sister 16.5% (16.0); FT│25.7% (25.8); PT 24.0% (20.7); female 26.1% (25.5); male 19.0% (15.4); all nurses 25.3% (24.9). Allowance for the number of hours worked actually produces few changes in the crude separation rates already described. The staff nurse rate, however, increases further, as do those for part-timers and male nurses.

18. Mercer, 'Fluctuations over Time in the Rate of Nursing Turnover'.

19. B. Pettman, 'External and Personal Determinants of Labour Turnover' in B. Pettman (ed.), *Labour Turnover and Retention* (Gower, London 1975), ch.2.

20. A.K. Rice, J.M. Hill and E.L. Trist, 'The Representation of Labour Turnover as a Social Process', *Human Relations*, vol.3 (1950), pp.358-9.

21. Ibid., p.356.

22. Ibid., pp.349-50.

23. Briggs, *Report of the Committee on Nursing*, ch.5.

24. Some in fact become agency nurses and are then asked to work in the NHS. See too Sadler and Whitworth, *Reserves of Nurses.*

25. A. Harris, *Labour Mobility in Great Britain* (HMSO, London, 1963).

26. P. Dixon and A. Pace, 'Manpower Planning' in E. Raybould (ed.), *A Guide for Nurse Managers* (Blackwell, London, 1977), ch.8.

27. Harris, *Labour Mobility in Great Britain.*

4   THE CHARACTER AND DETERMINANTS
       OF NURSING TURNOVER

The next step in our discussion involves an analysis of the conditions under which nursing turnover takes place. Our aim is to isolate those factors which, alone or together, determine whether nurses leave, or stay in, their current employment. But first we shall prepare the ground for the multivariate analysis by examining several different approaches to labour turnover. We want to establish which variables are worthy of inclusion in a study of nursing turnover, how much effect they exert, and in what ways. Three main standpoints in the study of labour turnover have won support. They are: (1) the economic, or labour market, account; (2) the institutional or 'culture of the firm' stance; and (3) the broader social and/or psychological approach.[1] The view adopted here is more eclectic, as we have combined structural factors with the expressed attitudes and motivations of those under scrutiny.

We begin with the economic or labour market interpretation of labour turnover, which is appropriate if only because it has exercised a profound and continuing sway on studies in this area — even when the investigation has been conducted by a non-economist.[2] Economic conditions are regarded as primary, but the central point is that labour mobility is deemed 'wage sensitive' to a quite significant degree. This is a throwback to traditional economic theory. The assumption is that the sensitivity of differential wage rates will push or pull labour between areas/employers/industries/occupations and so forth as the labour market adjusts to the oscillations of supply and demand. Equilibrium only arrives when there is no inducement to move. Certain discrepancies between the real world and this model are recognised even by its adherents, but their basic faith in its precepts is rarely confused. As described by Hicks, even when differences between regional wage rates exist, the pressure of the market is towards their elimination. Other economists have attempted to adapt Keynes's modification of orthodox economic theory to labour market studies.[3] They argue that the employment market has not been self-adjusting, but has instead lapsed into a downward spiral where the disparities between the advantaged and the disadvantaged are multiplied. The solution rests with massive state intervention to assist the depressed areas.

Yet despite their differences, these explanations all rely on an

economic explanation of labour mobility. The surprise is then, given
this widespread consensus, that the empirical verification of this
influence of wage rates on labour mobility has been conspicuously
meagre. In a series of investigations that stretch back to the depression
years during the 1930s at least, the impact of differential wage rates
has been downgraded. The lid, once raised, has let loose a flood of
qualifying conditions. In an early study in Britain the impediments to
mobility were adjudged to include

> the decision to work in a new environment among strange people;
> the business of moving one's home and family; the task of settling
> down (perhaps to a new occupation) with new workmates, new
> employers and even new conditions of work; and finally the process
> of making fresh contacts for the pursuit of social and intellectual
> activities.[4]

This echoes the view expressed by Alfred Marshall that the sensitivity
of the labour market was to 'net economic advantages'. 'We must take
account of the facts that one trade is healthier or cleanlier than another,
that it is carried on in a more wholesome or pleasant locality, or that
it involves a better social position.'[5] The scene has clearly long since
been set for a continuing debate about the merits of an embattled wage
rate champion and a host of contenders for that title.

Yet for many writers the impact of the labour market on mobility if
checked, is not denied. For example, Reynolds and Taft argue that the
absence of 'rational economic behaviour' is 'partly because of ignorance
and inertia, partly because of a sensible concern with security of tenure
and other benefits which come from long employment in the same
enterprise'. Secondly, there is a 'strong conventional element in workers'
judgement of an adequate wage rate'. Thirdly, there is the upheaval
caused by the

> appearance of new industries, and technical development of new
> areas of the country etc. . .It is thus possible for a wage differential
> to remain consistently larger than it would have been under static
> equilibrium, always tending to shrink toward the equilibrium level
> but not succeeding because of the rapid sweep of economic events.[6]

Myers is another reluctant to throw the labour market account away
entirely. He concludes a review of a number of American studies that
there is 'considerable haphazard and apparently purposeless movement,

many imperfections, and a weak link between mobility and the equalisation of net advantages'.[7] Increasingly the norm is one of complex shifts of industry, occupation and employer all at one time. Yet Myers still detects 'an internal flexibility in the American labour force which corresponds roughly with the theoretical model of a labour market within which workers move in response to differences in net advantages'. The role of personal and institutional factors is reduced to 'certain local labour markets and at particular times'.[8]

Such conclusions swim against a rather considerable tide of opinion that is more ready to ditch the wage-sensitive explanation of labour mobility. Lind summarises the alternatives as follows:

> To move towards a relative explanation of migration, one has to take into account a number of other economic variables (for example congestion or the state of an area's infrastructure) as well as geographic factors (for example the distance from the nearest major population centre), psychological factors (for example the 'image' of an area) and political factors (for example new towns or development area policy.[9]

The 'pure' labour market account has here collapsed before a seemingly inexhaustible flood of sociological and psychological speculation which constitutes a complex mediating apparatus that interrupts the hitherto direct link between wage levels and labour mobility.

Nevertheless the economic account has recently been reasserted in a comparatively undiluted form as an explanation couched in terms of a 'local labour market', or even an 'internal labour market' within a specific organisation. It is the former which has particularly assumed the mantle of wage rates' influence on labour mobility, although here too the detractors have become increasingly vocal. The position is further complicated by an inability among commentators to agree on the constitution of a local labour market. According to Kerr, it is a market 'with specific occupational, industrial and geographic boundaries, and with rules affecting entry, movement within and exit'.[10] It extends over that area from which a firm recruits its labour, and includes other firms with whom it is in competition for staff.[11] Unfortunately the empirical realisation of this phenomenon has proven far from straightforward, and its spatial boundaries have been especially elusive. It is not so difficult to establish the geographical constituency currently encompassed by a work-force, but the limits become extremely flexible when it is the potential pool of recruits under study. We have indicated previously that the recruitment net for trained nurses varies between registered and enrolled grades, which implies an occupational as much as a spatial limitation. In addition, nurse recruitment is heavily influenced by economic conditions, age, marital status, sex, age of children, travel distance to work and so forth, all of which undercut the influence of differential wage rates.

The internal labour market is less contentiously restricted to the boundaries of a specific organisation. The notion has attracted interest because of the manner in which it focuses on the pattern of internal movement, such as transfers and promotions. Kerr's distinction between structured and structureless internal labour markets fixes on such questions.[12] The structured type is where those already employed by a firm receive preferential treatment when it comes to filling the more sought-after posts. 'Ports of entry' then designate those grades or occupations where outside recruitment is concentrated. This phenomenon has been relatively common in manufacturing industry, but in hospitals the picture appears more confused.[13] Our examination of accessions indicates that most entrants rank as straightforward replacements for those who have left, although there is scattered evidence that in some hospitals the practice of promoting one's own staff nurses and recruiting at this grade level from outside has established a foothold. With enrolled staff, one can ignore any thoughts of ports of entry, since the senior state enrolled nurse posts are so few, although these are typically filled by internal promotion. The wider implication of the ports of entry thesis is that where it operates the lower grades in the nursing hierarchy will display relatively higher rates of turnover, and shorter lengths of service. In practice, staff nurses who stand to benefit most from remaining in post enjoy such reasonable prospects of advancement by going to another hospital that any structure in the internal market remains latent.

The presumption that the location of an organisation in two labour markets, one local and the other internal, confers extra possibilities for employers to ensure that labour is more sensitive to fluctuations in wage rates is difficult to sustain. On this point, Robinson concludes that

there is much variation in the level of average earnings of members of the same occupation in different firms in the same locality. There is also marked variation in the increases in these earnings. While in general there appears to be no very marked relationship between the changes in earnings in a particular firm and changes in the number employed in that occupation, in a few cases some relationship can be found. The clearest example is where a firm is [considerably expanding its work-force] . . .Even here, the changes in average earnings of an occupation which is increasing in numbers will not necessarily increase at the same rate as another expanding occupation in that firm. This could suggest that some firms do differentiate the increases in occupational earnings according to the supply position of that occupation. In other cases internal institutional pressures may prevent this.[14]

Another British study is emphatic that the assumptions about wage rates in the local labour market are not substantiated. While chaos does not rule, it comes close to reigning.[15]

A local labour market implies, for example, that employers and employees have accurate, up-to-date information on the state of the market. In contrast, most investigations conclude that the knowledge base on both sides is very incomplete, if not also incorrect. Ignorance and inertia are two reasons why people are immobile, but in addition there is a strong sense of customary rates and differentials which sometimes dilutes the comparison of wage levels.

It may legitimately be argued that the situation of nursing employment in the UK devalues any force which the local labour market exerts over other workers. To start with, the NHS is effectively in a monopsonist position with respect to the employment of nurses. The 1971 census reported that less than 2 per cent of all trained nurses currently in nursing are working outside the NHS. Not only are other nursing opportunities restricted, but they are concentrated in more basic nursing, and tend to offer little scope for a career or advancement. The contrast in nursing remuneration between the public and private sector is therefore an empty exercise. Of course, nurses may be more tempted by better prospects in other occupations to quit nursing, but even then there are good reasons why inertia will prevail. They have already invested several years' training to be a nurse which will be 'wasted' if they leave, while it is usually the case within the professions that benefits accrue the longer the length of service. Short-term gains have then to be set against long-term advantages of staying in nursing.

It is more probable with a professional group which undergoes a period of several years' obligatory training that the impact of what is perceived as unfair or unreasonable remuneration will be felt not so much in a high mobility to other work, but in a reduced flow of new trainees. This raises questions about the effect of wage rates in occupational choice, particularly among women, since nursing has long been regarded as a 'natural' career for a young girl to pursue. Yet the range of occupations which women are encouraged to join is expanding and nursing is increasingly in competition for suitable recruits. Hence the comparison of its wage rates with other areas assumes greater significance. But for those already in the service, the question as posed consists more of a choice between staying in nursing or not working at all, rather than moving to a better-paid occupation. Like any other people, nurses cannot pay their bills and live on what many regard as the high status of their profession, or its high job satisfaction, but these have proven weighty bulwarks against leaving the NHS to work elsewhere.

The circumstances of male nurses, while similar in several important respects, diverge sufficiently to resurrect thoughts of the economic account.[16] The claim is that males, because of their position as the family breadwinner (typically), are under more pressure to follow the money, and therefore exhibit a lower threshold for quitting. But even if we accept that male nurses place a higher premium on financial incentives, there are sound reasons to suppose that they are no more instrumental in their orientation to work than other male workers, and probably less so.

Such considerations imply that the labour market account — whether in its national, local or internal guise — is severely breached when applied to the specific circumstances of trained nurses in the National Health Service. If the economic explanation, in its pure form, is overstated, this is partly due to the almost universal generalisation that labour turnover is strongly associated with employment levels. The commendably forthright statement of March and Simon proclaims,

> Under nearly all conditions the most accurate single predictor of labour turnover is the state of the economy. Even such a gross aggregate as the national quit rate shows a strong negative relationship with the aggregate rate of discharges and layoffs.[17]

In Britain, Behrend sums up the position as follows, 'The stick — the fear of unemployment — is probably still the most effective incentive we know for reducing labour turnover and absenteeism.'[18] The threat is more intense if unemployment is looming in the industry or area where the individual is located. The correlation figures between unemployment and departure rates reported by Wild and Dawson of 0.5 and 0.4 for males and females respectively in manufacturing industry compare with our combined level of 0.3, but this is enhanced if job vacancies are also taken into account.[19] Nevertheless, this still leaves us short of a full explanation of the process at work. From our previous discussion of the effect of economic conditions, we are tempted to argue that trained nurses are relatively more immune — in the direct sense — than many others from the threat of forced redundancies and dismissals, but they will be equally restricted in any ambition to move outside the NHS, and will be inhibited from quitting work temporarily because of a threat to their husband's job, or perhaps because they fear that there will be no vacancy to come back to when they want to return.

The fear in criticising the economic account is that we throw out the baby with the bathwater. Its limitations have none the less given rise to institutional as well as more extensive 'net advantages' approaches. Myers[20] pinpoints the research interest for labour mobility in the following: (1) the manner of occupational choice, both initially and subsequently; (2) the characteristic pattern of movement between firms/occupations/regions; and (3) the characteristics of those who are more inclined to move than stay put. Each of these foci extends the explanation of labour turnover considerably, and raises much wider questions about the individual's whole orientation to work.

In the initial entry into employment, the usual indications are that individuals take a much larger spread of factors into account than those which offer the highest financial rewards. The balance of informed opinion is that occupational selection usually takes shape over many years, while there are crossroads that have to be negotiated which help narrow down this choice.[21] However, these decisions are often made without full knowledge of the situation or alternative possibilities, and when a course is adopted, the reasons offered indicate that 'net advantages' are very broadly interpreted. The influence of family and friends is most important and in both manual and non-manual occupations there is often a widely accepted practice that children follow in the steps of their father or mother. This self-recruitment is especially evident in the professions.[22] While this pattern is most clearly drawn in the initial entry on to the labour market, the influence of immediate contacts continues, but increasingly from friends rather than relatives. Whatever the lines of communication about the labour market, it is argued that the individual

has no idea of the full range of jobs, wage rates and working conditions prevailing in the area; nor does he (she) have any realisation of the hundreds of thousands of job vacancies available

on a particular day. At most he (she) knows about a few jobs which
have come to his (her) attention,

through the essentially haphazard mechanism of informal contact.[23]
Reynolds goes on to argue that occupational comparison once in the
labour market consists of dividing jobs into those worth taking and
others which are not. This evaluation is based on certain minimum
standards expected from work, rather than a detailed checklist of
valued attributes. There is therefore little notion of a hierarchy of
preferred occupations. 'If he comes across a "good" job, he takes it
without worrying over whether a "better" job may be available
somewhere else.'[24] This orientation is perhaps more apparent among
those with few marketable skills, and whose job horizons are more
restricted to those areas where there are relatively few differences
between jobs. However, it is this same manual sector which has always
suffered most from unemployment and which is understandably more
unwilling to decline a job offer when it can mean gambling with the
family's well-being.

Nurses, in contrast, are one of those groups who are widely thought
to have made a choice on the merits of the job. The ambition of many
women to enter the profession is nevertheless a long-standing one. At
least one-third of all females are estimated to seriously consider nursing
as a career, although for many young girls 'nursing' can cover a wide
range of activities.[25] Most studies have concluded that the attraction
of the profession lies in the opportunities it offers for service to others,
or its intrinsic qualities.[26] Moreover, girls are encouraged to 'play at
being a nurse', and there is a steady emphasis throughout their
formative years on the parallels between the skills of a woman/mother
and a nurse. Yet while the positive appeal of nursing among women
cannot be belittled, it is also true that the range of employment
opportunities for women is considerably restricted compared with men.
For the latter, nursing is a less 'obvious' occupation to choose; part of
this is due to the popular view of nursing as a 'woman's job', and part
is attributable to the better prospects that are believed to lie
elsewhere.[27] In consequence, a much higher proportion of men are
expected to have had work experience outside nursing or the Health
Service. Whatever their path of entry, individuals do not enter work
with a clean slate, but instead begin with an assortment of values,
expectations and attitudes which sometimes aid, sometimes hinder
their assimilation into the organisation or work in general. Thus these
are legitimate subjects for inclusion as potential predictors of labour

turnover.

Our interest is only in actual departures, rather than individuals' latent desires, and within this number we distinguish between leavers in terms of the direction they take after quitting. We have seen in the previous chapter that there is a considerable divide between basically two groups — one which leaves the service for domestic reasons, and which gives up work altogether, and a second category which is merely mobile between NHS hospital posts. The interesting point is whether different conditions underlie these categories, or if essentially the same set of factors determine mobility whatever direction is followed.

Several contributions worthy of note have been made to this debate. For example, Palmer argues that the direction of labour mobility is an important consideration in any explanation or prediction of turnover since the several types may be arranged into a hierarchy according to the complexity of factors which enter the decision.[28] She designates changes in employer as the most straightforward in normal circumstances, while complications multiply as the mobility covers changes in occupation, industry and place of residence. The rationale behind this scheme is that labour mobility is particularly influenced, first, by the sharpness with which occupations and industries are differentiated, and secondly, by the extent to which boundary lines are reinforced by conditions of entry such as qualifications, apprenticeship and previous experience. We believe that nursing constitutes one such well defined occupation which greatly influences the ease and desirability of movement. But because of the large number of women in the service and the particular domination of nursing employment in Britain by the NHS, a design taken from private manufacturing industry does not sit easily with nursing turnover. It has already been demonstrated that nurses are much given to moving between hospitals (employers), but that they are strongly disinclined to take up other employment. Of that small minority who leave the NHS for new pastures, more stay with nursing but in a different 'industry' rather than move into another occupation. Palmer's hierarchy is also overturned in the greater readiness of nurses to be geographically mobile — a characteristic which is greatly encouraged by the opportunities offered in NHS employment. The potentially greater trauma of moving one's home is in practice counterbalanced by the relative ease with which a nurse will acclimatise to a new hospital environment. The grand omission from this account, however, is the absence of a category which allows for leaving work temporarily. In nursing the training period will tend to tie worker and employer together so that both benefit as it is recognised that taking a break from work is no bar to returning later when individual circumstances permit.

The discussion this far has hinged on the reasons why people move, but consideration of why people remain in a particular occupation is equally relevant to an explanation of labour turnover. All too often the literature emphasises the forces for movement and ignores the often strong pressures towards stability. A possible attachment is towards the community in which one lives, and perhaps works. This link can outweigh the connection to an employer or to an occupation.[29] Jeffreys recounts how 'change of residence encouraged change of occupation rather than the reverse.'[30] This implies that female nurses who are forced to leave because their husband has been transferred to another part of the country are more inclined to try another occupation or nurse outside the NHS. But much of this is perhaps due to the lack of nursing vacancies in the areas to which they have moved. Links with kin and a wide circle of friends are widely mentioned as discouragements to geographical mobility, while the availability of suitable accommodation (at the right price) is another important consideration in the decision whether or not to migrate to a new district. Not surprisingly, young, single people appear disproportionately in the lists of migrants. This is as true of nurses as other occupations. Indeed it is sometimes claimed that the potential for mobility around the country offered by nursing is an important perk of the job. Even for those who do not intend to change employers, there is often a strong pressure to conform to 'usual nursing practice'. This will be a part of the strong roots which professionals are presumed to spread in their chosen field. They will become deeply imbued with nursing and hospital culture, such is the force of their training and general socialisation. The heart of this process lies in 'the silent dialogue wherein are fused person, situation, and institution'.[31] For the Tavistock model this leads to a 'settled connexion', but, as our own data demonstrate, any settledness is with nursing rather than individual hospitals.

Myers's final point about possible clues to understanding labour turnover rests with the characteristics of those who stay and leave. Several comments relevant to this area have already been made in passing. For example, age, sex, marital status, social background and educational qualifications all have had their champions, but the effect of each is invariably mediated by their interrelationship and their interaction with a host of other forces. One specific conclusion in the literature, however, is that a small group in the work-force accounts for a disproportionate amount of the mobility. Research into the behaviour of employees in Battersea and Dagenham indicates that over a six-year period, the majority of those contacted had moved jobs only once or twice. 'Only one in six of the total labour force had changed three or four times, and only three in every hundred had changed, on the average, once or more every year.'[32] This means that as few as 3 per cent of the work-force produced some 20 per cent of all moves. Similar concentrations arise in nursing, where |23.6 per cent of nurses produce 52.4 per cent of post changes, and a mere 6 per cent of staff accumulate over 50 per cent of the hospital mobility. However, frequency of labour mobility between occupations or employers is not the same as geographical mobility in the eyes of these regular movers. The occasional mover is as likely as anyone to choose the long-distance option, while the flitters keep within fairly narrow spatial limits.[33] The intention now is to identify within this sometimes bewildering array of influences on labour turnover which exactly justify inclusion in our case study of trained nurses.

Review of Potential Determinants of Nursing Turnover

A number of excellent reviews of the correlates and predictors of labour turnover exist and three in particular have been a rich source of ideas in our case study. These are by March and Simon, Pettman and Price.[34] The reader who consults Figures 4.1 and 4.2 will appreciate that our discussion is not a complete overview. The main sources plundered here are additionally useful because they go beyond a listing of possible associations to a considered organisation of the hypotheses. Our classification separates those factors which influence the ease of movement, and others which affect its desirability. It is sometimes hard to sustain this division in practice, but it does encompass an important analytical distinction, and contains the added benefit that it follows a well established tradition in turnover research.[35]

Desirability of Movement

Probably the major influence according to most commentators on the desire to move is job satisfaction, irrespective of whether this is treated as a single factor or as composed of several elements. Though the notion of job satisfaction enjoys wide popular and academic currency, it has proven most elusive to those intent on its operationalisation.[36] People diverge on what they regard as the most important components in building a favourable view of work and particular work roles. March

Figure 4.1: Factors Affecting the Desirability of Movement

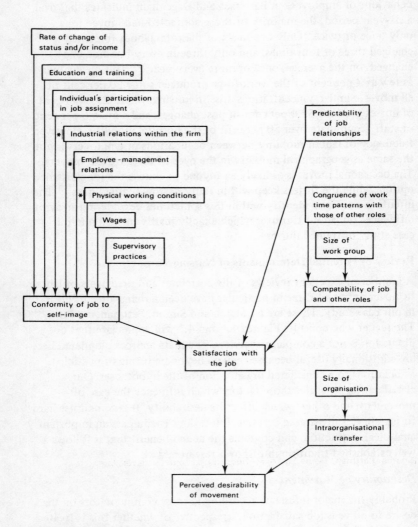

*Additions to March and Simon

Source: B. Pettman, 'Some Factors Influencing Labour Turnover: a Review of Research Literature', *Industrial Relations*, vol.4 (1973), pp.43-61.

Figure 4.2: Factors Affecting the Ease of Movement

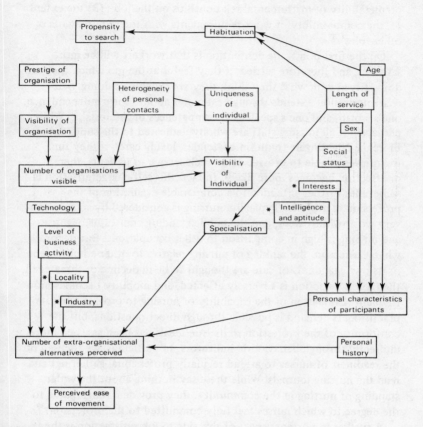

*Additions to March and Simon.

Source: Pettman, 'Some Factors Influencing Labour Turnover', p.45.

and Simon attempt a categorisation along the following lines: (1) the extent of the 'conformity of the job characteristics to the self-characterisation held by the individual'; (2) the extent of 'the predictability of instrumental relationships on the job'; (3) the extent of 'the compatibility of work requirements with the requirements of other roles'.[37]

On the first point, the contention is that workers will be more satisfied, and therefore settled, if they feel that the job which they are doing fits in with what they think they are capable of doing. Self-characterisation extends through estimates about 'one's independence, one's worth, and one's specialised competences or interests'.[38] While perhaps not all nursing staff are wholly dedicated to the supposed Florence Nightingale tradition of 'tender, loving care', if they find themselves unable to provide some such service to patients, then disaffection becomes more likely. In fact, this self-characterisation is sometimes further extended to a comparable evaluation of the profession as a whole. Typically, nursing is considered by society as a very worthwhile career, and the public standing and status of nurses and nursing is high in comparison to other occupations. But if, for whatever reason, the ranking of nursing relative to other employment or its own standards of care are thought to be in decline or threatened, then job satisfaction is adversely affected, and mobility becomes more frequent. Evaluation of the capability of nursing to provide what its practitioners demand is possible through direct questions, but the conformity of the profession to its true ideals has been assessed more indirectly through behavioural indicators. In particular, we focused on the readiness of nurses to attend regularly professional gatherings and read the nursing journals. While these say nothing about the wider standing of nursing in the community, they provide a rough guide to the degree to which nurses feel fully committed to the profession.[39]

A further important aspect of this side to job satisfaction is the nature of the supervisory practices.[40] There is a considerable body of research which highlights the conflict between the workers' desire for some degree of job autonomy against managements' demand for adequate supervision. Whether the latter can be turned into a sufficiently considerate and participative style that will satisfy both sides is a moot point, but if work control is regarded as unreasonably restrictive then the probability of mobility becomes greater.[41] Self-characterisation also involves an assessment whether the 'amount of rewards earned' — above all financial, but also including other fringe benefits and status improvements — are considered an accurate and reasonable valuation.[42] Those who feel that they are relatively poorly rewarded in comparison to others in their organisation, or in society generally, will be more inclined to turn their thoughts to trying other work. In our questionnaire, we followed the suggestion by Price that the peer group comparison indulged in by nurses is with: (1) other nurses of their grade; (2) other groups outside nursing; while the perception of distributive justice extends to: (3) the effort put into the job; and (4) the contribution made to running the hospital.[43]

Another frequent explanation of the perceived desirability of movement is that a higher level of education engenders greater aspirations for 'getting on'.[44] In much the same way, the rate of advancement in rewards that is looked for can affect job stability if the former drops below anticipated levels. If, for example, promotion prospects are depressed, or much less than originally envisaged, within the hospital or compared with elsewhere, then discontent and departure become more likely.[45] Additional influences in this general area comprise the physical conditions of the work. Undue physical exertion, or working in dirty, noisy or dangerous conditions also undermine stability in work.[46]

Many aspects of self-characterisation derive from the individual's location in the social structure, and the varying pressures to conform under which people find themselves. Our impression is that nursing imposes rather more constraints on its members than many occupations, and this can affect the desirability of movement if it is felt that the demands of nursing are overly restrictive. Nurses want to have a reasonable social and home life, but at some point they may feel that 'the congruence of work time patterns with those of other roles' is too remote.[47] For example, the typical working day is a nine to five routine, five days a week, but nurses are liable to work at weekends and holidays, as well as any of the 24 hours in the day. This may not weigh too heavily in their early years, but as the breadth of domestic commitments extends, night work or attendance at other 'anti-social' times is likely to affect the wish to stay as adversely among nurses as it apparently does among manufacturing workers.[48] The possibility of role conflict along these lines is especially strong in a female work-force. March and Simon conspicuously ignore the particular difficulties of women in work, and especially those with a family to look after as well. Since the female role is supposed to give priority to home/housework, the number and type of hours worked become crucial. A few women obtain support for their dual role, but for the majority, when a clash occurs, the result is often a move to cut the number of hours worked or, more drastically, a departure from work altogether.

Other elements which we link together in this account are the 'size of the work group' and the 'size of the organisation'.[49] The influence on turnover exerted by the size of the hospital in which the nurse is located stems basically from the greater centralisation and bureaucratisation which larger organisations are supposed to display.[50] With the rise in employment concentration, there is a stronger possibility that the individual employee will feel lost — or 'anomic'. The impression gained is that they are treated increasingly as numbers rather than human beings, and that red tape has increased so drastically that they are unable to nurse properly. The effect of the size of the group in which the individual works has given rise to some celebrated research. For example, Mayo and Lombard declared that there is a positive spin-off for job stability if workers are able to develop meaningful relationships with those in close proximity to them.[51] This notion has been widely recommended in the Health Service, where it is argued that interdependent team work among all of the hospital workers will greatly stimulate employee morale. In practice, there is sometimes a gap between the enthusiasm with which such schemes have been advocated and their actual realisation on the wards. We have therefore re-interpreted the size of the work group to the nature of the specialism in which they are involved in their hospital work. This is necessary since numbers on a ward are neither sufficiently stable nor so different across departments, and specialism is more likely to capture differences in the style of employee contacts. At one extreme, those on nights, who often cover more than one ward, and who engage in a different routine, are likely to be less immersed in close work relationships than those on a specialism such as maternity.[52] These organisational issues also stretch into the 'perceived possibility of intraorganisational transfer', where the lack of opportunities for internal movement in the smaller organisations will necessitate external mobility.[53]

Ease of Movement

The second branch of the turnover tree spreads around the availability of jobs, for which individuals may reasonably apply. This ease of labour mobility has already been referred to on several occasions, and it has been emphasised that while there is an overall association between turnover and economic conditions there is sufficient variation in this relationship to warrant many refinements in the basic proposition.

To start with, the greater 'the number of perceived

extraorganisational alternatives', the more likely the individual is to view mobility as a realistic option. In nursing, the short supply of staff in many areas and the often rapid turnover of personnel has given rise to a presumption that movement to another hospital will create few difficulties. There are some well recognised instances where the ease of movement has a geographical dimension — London is often offered as a case in point — or is easier in some specialisms, such as theatre staff.[54]

The characteristics and circumstances of the individual nurse also rank as significant influences on the perceived ease of movement. The typical conclusion of turnover studies has been that women workers display a higher rate of instability than men, although when men and women from the same backgrounds and occupations have been considered this variation usually disappears for the most part.[55] This implies that the explanation stems not from sex differences but from the contrasting pressures on men and women in work. Female turnover has therefore been further associated with marital status, and whether they have any children, and if so, their ages.[56] To be single and without domestic ties is to increase the opportunities for movement. In a similar fashion the age of the individual has an impact, since the younger persons are most able to pack up their bags and go elsewhere. For older people, the balance of advantages is more tilted in favour of stability, certainly geographically. To pull up roots usually takes one away from family, friends and familiar places, while a change in occupation or employer while remaining in the same vicinity can threaten promotion prospects, fringe benefits and pension rights. Quite simply, the older the individual, the less mobile they become.[57]

The perceived range of job alternatives is also a function of the social class or status of the worker. The explanation advanced is that those from higher social backgrounds, or those in more prestigious occupations, take a wider view of outside opportunities, at least for themselves. In part it is a question of the extension of opportunities in non-manual occupations, but it is also probably related to the lower level of community ties maintained among non-working-class groups. This has led to the growth of distinctions between 'spiralists' and 'burgesses', with the former characterised as geographically and socially mobile, while the latter are more fixed.[58] Social standing is also connected to occupational location of the spouse — meaning essentially in our study the nurse's husband. For most married women the husband's job is accorded priority, and if this necessitates movement to another part of the country the wife's career is most likely to suffer — although perhaps not as much in nursing as with some less transferable occupational skills. The occupation of the marriage partner can therefore be a factor in the perceived ease of movement, so that if we take the opposite side of the coin, those nurses married to teachers will be less inhibited from movement compared to those married to members of the armed forces.[59]

Parallel social forces may lead to a different perception of the ease of movement between ethnic groups. We hypothesise that those nurses from abroad, mainly because they have fewer local ties, will be more inclined to take advantage of this lack of constraint on their movement.[60]

The most frequently mentioned correlate of labour turnover is the length of completed service in current post. Its effect among nurses has already been examined sufficiently in this study to warrant its further analysis against a much wider range of influence and controls. The nature of its impact is typically experienced in an early peak of departures, with a more settled connection developing over time as work and colleagues become more familiar, and the incentives to stay increase. Long-service workers will however become more fixed in their positions, and therefore will be less sought after by other employers. Length of service's influence in nursing is circumscribed by the skill or grade level attained, but horizontal movement is less severely affected than in many occupations because nursing is a skill which travels well.[61]

Ease of movement is again facilitated by a sound knowledge, or 'visibility of organisations'. To nurses, some hospitals have a noteworthy attraction because of their perceived prestige or glamour — perhaps because of a specialist unit, its medical prowess, or more generally because it is regarded as a good place to nurse. While there are reasons to doubt whether nurses, like others, keep track of job openings far beyond their immediate workplace, there are several mechanisms which should stimulate their awareness of relevant alternatives. One factor is the nature and frequency of contact with their nursing colleagues, which encompasses attendance at professional gatherings and the regular reading of nursing journals. The individuals most heavily involved in these activities are more able to acquire that information and those contacts which make movement easier.[62]

Less easily contained in the questionnaire format is March and Simon's suggestion of an 'explicitly motivational factor' which defines a personality type that is less disturbed by the prospect of regular movements.[63] Since we have previously decided not to explore this psychological dimension, we cannot cover their specific recommendation, although we have included references to the number of posts and hospitals occupied. In this sense, scope is provided for previous work record to influence mobility levels among nurses.

While this discussion has concentrated on the factors reported in March and Simon's review, there are additional factors whose influence in turnover research recommends their inclusion here. We have extended the number of job attitudes, and have introduced as possible influences type of housing, distance of travel to work, membership of secondary associations — both within and outside nursing — as well as attitudes to women's role in society.[64]

We remind the reader that although this listing of the influences to be tested in our case study of nursing turnover has proceeded variable by variable, the objective behind our statistical analysis is to assess their impact both individually and collectively. To sum up: we collected information in our case study on a wide range of 'independent' variables or 'predictors', which are treated as potential 'causes' of high or low values on our 'dependent' variable — that is, whether the individual nurse stayed in or left the current place of employment in the period covered by our investigation. To this end we have cast our net widely and included not only immediate workplace circumstances, but also many social, domestic and personal factors.

Multivariate Analysis of Nursing Turnover

In a study where the number of candidate predictors of labour turnover is limited, data computation and analysis are relatively straightforward, even if the complexity of 'real life' is ignored. The typical social survey now presents a contrary problem because of the irresistible temptation to collect veritable mountains of data. Our requirement is a data analysis strategy which can cope with a large number of variables — as outlined above — although the end product for which we are searching is a model of nursing turnover which is altogether more parsimonious.

The main analytical procedure employed is the multiple regression routine contained in the Statistical Package for the Social Sciences (SPSS). Not that we jumped straight away into this. Instead we carried out a detailed inspection of the data to ensure that it suited the regression analysis. We have been reassured by the comments of others that multiple regression assumptions do not demand interval level measurement, but can cope with nominal data even; and secondly, although dependent variables should usually be continuous, statisticians accept that regression analysis with a dichotomous dependent variable is not an outrageous proposition. The predictions then generated are of 'expected proportions'.[65] Of the other assumptions contained in regression analysis, the most frequently emphasised are that the researcher recognises the need for: additivity, linearity and an absence of interaction effects. The regression output supplied by SPSS can be used to sort out such problems, but we have made especial use of an analysis of variance technique recommended by Sonquist and Morgan.[66] Their programme generates a tree-like effect of two-way splits, which supply information on the differential impact of the predictors across a variety of subgroups compared with the original population. If interaction effects, or patterns of cumulation and substitution are revealed, the data are more inappropriate for multiple regression analysis, unless some modifications in the data are introduced. The interested reader is referred to other places where these preliminaries were pursued at some length on our data.[67] Suffice to say that the more gross imperfections have been eliminated — notably, interaction effects — and henceforward we shall concentrate on the multiple regression analysis itself.

The first step is to list the final set of predictors that remained from all those candidate variables discussed in the previous section. These are illustrated in subsequent tables, where they are grouped into three broad areas: (1) job features; (2) job attitudes; and (3) personal and domestic circumstances.[68] Perhaps it is worthwhile to run through those variables which did not generate sufficient effect to warrant further inclusion in the final stages of our multivariate analysis. Just as the majority of candidate predictors comprised job attitudes so these loom largest among the ranks of the rejected. The latter include items on the amount of rewards received; questions about the level of interference from supervisors in the individual's work routine; on the worth and competence of nurses and nursing, and on its perceived standing with the public. Out too go items on the readership of nursing journals, along with estimations of the prestige and visibility of other organisations. Among the job features, membership of a professional association or a union and the number of breaks from nursing prove irrelevant. Several domestic and personal characteristics similarly fall by the wayside. These include items on the social background of the nurses, and the occupation of their spouse, as well as their nationality. Attitudes towards the role of women in society, whether at home or in work, all lapse. And of the locality variables, community ties, travel distance to work and membership of organisations outside the hospital fail to discriminate between nurses in their turnover behaviour.

These omitted, a final group of 22 predictors remained.[69] These were used in the first regression run where the dependent variable is whether the individual nurse stayed or left. The first indicator of the

Table 4.1: Multiple Regression Statistics for Predictors of Nursing Turnover

Predictors	Simple r	R^2 change	Unstandardised regression coefficients	Standardised regression coefficients
Size of hospital	−.16	.02	−.05	−.08
Length of service	−.26	.17	−.04	−.07
Number of hospitals worked at	−.06	.001	−.01	−.02
Hours worked	−.05	.004	−.002	−.004
Ward (specialism)	−.09	.004	−.007	−.01
Shift worked	−.12	.005	−.02	−.02
Grade	−.10	.004	−.04	−.08
Sex	−.05	.003	−.03	−.03
Age	−.24	.001	−.001	−.003
Education	.21	.003	.06	.07
Marital status	−.09	.001	.06	.06
Has youngster(s)	−.15	.004	−.08	−.08
Organisational satisfaction	.04	.001	.01	−.03
Amenability of supervision	.11	.003	.02	.05
Communication	.15	.002	.01	.05
Pay-effort comparison	−.07	.001	.007	.01
Promotion prospects	−.06	.005	−.03	−.06
Other job opportunities	−.10	.001	−.02	−.03
Future work intentions	−.51	.21	−.18	−.46
Career satisfaction	−.02	.005	−.05	−.08

$R^2 = 31$; F = 16.9; df = 36
Standard error = 0.37

effect of these predictors lies in the total amount of variance explained by their collective effect. This is the R^2 figure contained in Table 4.1. It adds up to 31 per cent. In addition, the level of significance, as shown in the F ratio and degrees of freedom (df) are included. For each predictor, there are four statistics: (1) the simple r, which is the correlation coefficient between that variable and the dependent variable; (2) the R^2 change, which signifies the amount of variance contributed by each individual predictor; (3) the unstandardised regression coefficient; and (4) the standardised regression coefficient. These last two specify the amount of effect attributable to each factor after

112 The Character and Determinants of Nursing Turnover

controlling for the effect of all others — in the latter case after
standardising the values of the individual variables.

There can be no doubt about which predictor has the greatest effect
in producing variation in nursing turnover — the nurse's own expression
of their future work intentions. To ask no more of nurses than whether
they will be staying in post or leaving during the next year provides by
far the most accurate guide to their actual behaviour during this time.
After this the hierarchy of effect declines substantially, and the
remaining predictors group into two discernible layers. Within the
second band are the following: size of hospital, length of service,
educational level, grade, marital status, has young children, career
satisfaction, promotion prospects, extent of supervision and job
communication. Below these, but not by a large margin, we place:
number of hospitals worked at, shift, sex, organisational satisfaction
and other job opportunities. This leaves the remainder: hours worked,
ward specialism, age and the pay-effort comparison — with no
discernible influence on nursing turnover.

Most of these predictors at least influence the dependent variable
in the direction anticipated even if their effect is sometimes marginal.
If we take these one by one the following emerge from the standardised
regression coefficients as the more likely to depart:

(1)   those who work in the larger hospitals;
(2)   the nurses with the shorter length of service;
(3)   those who have worked at one/few hospital(s);
(4)   full-time staff;
(5)   those on general wards;
(6)   those working a shift other than nights;
(7)   women;
(8)   younger nurses;
(9)   the better qualified educationally;
(10)   married rather than single nurses;*
(11)   those without young children;
(12)   satisfied with overall organisation of the hospital;*
(13)   those unhappy with immediate supervisor;
(14)   those nurses who participate in regular meetings about their
       work;
(15)   those dissatisfied with pay-effort comparison;*
(16)   those who think promotion prospects are good;
(17)   those who think that there are plenty of nursing opportunities
       in other hospitals;

(18)   the more junior (staff) nurses;
(19)   those nurses who intend leaving;
(20)   those satisfied with nursing as a career.

(An asterisk (*) indicates that the direction of the relationship between the predictor and turnover reported is reversed if one compares the zero-order correlation coefficient with the regression statistic as reported above.)

Aside then from the future work intentions item there is a complex picture where job features, job attitudes and personal and domestic predictors all have a noteworthy effect on the dependent variable. The leavers' profile is of short-service |staff, in the larger hospitals, who are generally the better qualified. This educational item mirrors the impact of grade, for which it is anyway an alternative measure, given the slightly higher educational qualifications of registered staff compared with enrolled nurses. That the better qualified figure relatively more prominantly among the leavers is therefore not only a function of the differential grade departure rates, but also of the higher stability of the less well educated in each of the grades. The influence of domestic items is not always obvious. The greater leaving of married nurses contrasts with the usual image of the highly mobile as single persons, but against this, the lack of family constraints effect is anticipated. The widespread practice for leavers to quit work altogether has already been discussed, and there is support here for an explanation in terms of their domestic circumstances. Yet to further complicate the picture full-timers veer towards the leaving category, as do those working all shifts except nights.

The attitudinal predictors are perhaps a more obvious source of confusion, until, that is, one rejects the simple association of job satisfaction with desirability of movement. For in this analysis, those nurses who display the higher levels of satisfaction with their work across such areas as promotion prospects, organisational satisfaction, other opportunities and nursing generally — but not with pay or supervision — are more likely to move out. These include a large number who are taking another hospital post, but their decision to try a new place contains no obvious aspersions against |their old employer. If anything they are demonstrating their commitment to nursing, since the move has arisen because of the 'pull' of another institution or the promotion it is perhaps offering, rather than the 'push' of dissatisfying circumstances in their present hospital. Likewise, those who are giving up paid employment are not noticeably more likely to voice grouses about their current employment.

Overall, the amount of variation in the dependent variable explained by these predictors is not impressive. This is brought home even more if one realises that without the all-powerful future intentions predictor, the amount of variance is slashed to a paltry 14 per cent. The unavoidable conclusion is that those items included in our investigation are poor predictors of the simple division between stayers and leavers, at least in the whole group of trained nurses. Against this obvious interpretation, there are several alternative reasons which account for the negative outcome of this regression analysis. For example, other factors not obvious or included may have confounded the influence of the predictors on which we have reported; measurement error may have been greater than anticipated; or on another tack, twelve months may simply not be a long enough period for the predictors' effect to emerge, or conversely, perhaps this period is too long.[70]

In a similar vein, further analysis of the predictors taken individually rather than in combination reveals that several of these are, to a recognisable degree, substitutes for one another. This is implied by the larger variation which is generated when predictors are taken one by one. A few of the determinants, in other words, encapsulate more than one of the influences on turnover described here. The effect of grade, for example, is in some respects similar to the collective influence of such other variables as education level, age, marital status, previous work record and promotion prospects. To counter this specific shortcoming we constructed indices of job attitudes and of domestic circumstances. Nevertheless, there is latitude for more analysis along these lines.

Rather more immediate avenues for further exploration of the power of these predictors of nursing turnover arise in two areas. First, there is the argument that in taking as our subject the whole population of trained nurses we constituted an altogether too heterogeneous group to allow for proper discrimination between leavers and stayers. We have already demonstrated that turnover rates and length of service vary considerably between nurses according to their grade, hours worked, their sex and hospital. Mindful of this, it may transpire that conditions which have encouraged high mobility in one group are not the same as those which stimulate other leavers. A second explanation for the failure of the selected independent variables to predict turnover also attributes this to the congregation of all leavers into one group, when this time they might profitably be split according to the direction followed. We know that this group is fairly evenly distributed between

Table 4.2: Multiple Regression Statistics for Predictors of Nursing Turnover, by Grade

Predictors	SEN		Staff Nurse		Ward Sister/Charge Nurse	
	Simple r	Src[a]	r	Src	r	Src
Size of hospital	−.18	−.11	−.15	−.06	−.11	−.07
Length of service	−.12	−.07	−.22	−.02	−.13	−.03
Hours worked	−.03	.02	−.23	.05	.03	.02
Future work intent	−.45	−.42	−.54	−.48	−.44	−.42
Job satisfaction	.03	−.07	.05	−.03	.03	−.01
Supervision	.13	.08	.08	.03	.07	.06
Communication	−.13	−.06	−.12	−.04	.00	−.01
Pay and effort	.03	.09	−.17	−.08	.00	.05
Promotion	.03	−.01	−.18	−.06	−.07	−.07
Friends	−.14	−.10	.08	−.05	−.06	−.03
Other opportunities	−.08	−.03	−.14	−.03	−.03	−.01
Job commitment	.04	−.06	−.06	−.08	−.03	−.06
Sex	−.07	−.04	−.01	−.10	−.02	−.01
Marital status	−.13	.13	−.25	−.02	.07	.09
Children	−.26	−.17	−.26	−.05	−.05	−.06
Education	.20	.10	.28	.08	.16	.06
Living accommodation	.12	.03	.27	.04	−.03	−.02
R^2	.30		.35		.23	
Standard error	.37		.40		.33	
N	321		386		598	

a. Src = standardised regression coefficient.

those who stay in the NHS and those who give up work, albeit temporarily. It is perhaps naïve to suppose that the same set of reasons underlie mobility in two such contrasting directions. Therefore the second tactic is to break down the sample to assess the prediction of turnover direction.

In Table 4.2 the respondents have been divided by grade, sex and age. These controls induce a moderate response as far as the effect of the several predictors is concerned. With grade of nurse, the explained variation in nursing turnover ranges from 23 per cent for ward sisters and charge nurses, through 30 per cent for enrolled nurses, up to a high point of 35 per cent among staff nurses. The contrast in effect between male and female nurses is that the predictors explain more of the variation (38 per cent) in the case of the former. Conversely, the age split throws together a group of nurses aged 35 years and over, where the total variation drops substantially to only 19 per cent.

An examination of the respective strength of individual predictors furnishes several dramatic contrasts. There is no question whatsoever that the outstanding predictor of nursing turnover in each of the subgroups identified, as well as in the sample as a whole, is the nurses' own expression of their future work intentions. It is always at least twice as powerful as the next most powerful determinant, although again its level fluctuates across the several groups. Males and staff nurses are the most proficient at uniting intent and action, while the older nurses are notably less skilful in this respect. We interpret the relative success of the former in terms of the general lack of, or lower level of, constraints, both on the domestic front and at work, so that they are better able to plan definitely for their future movements.

The spread of effect across the remaining variables generally diverges markedly for each of the subgroups. Few of the predictors flourish across all of the categories, and some even manage to influence turnover from opposite directions. If we use enrolled nurses as the base, those working in larger hospitals, who are married and have no young children, who are relatively well qualified, and who have few friends at work, are marginally more probable leavers. In contrast, their registered colleagues offer few predictors with even this moderate impact. One exception occurs among staff nurses where females are more likely to move on, although this grade is studiously unimpressed by domestic variables. Ward sisters and charge nurses are another group more likely to leave if married, and again the size of the hospital exerts some influence. Equally significant, in the negative sense, is the relegation of job attitudes' impact. The pay-effort comparison and the nurses' reported job commitment are the only items to exhibit any general impression across the three grades. However, while enrolled staff and ward sisters who depart from their current post are relatively more satisfied with the rewards of the job, staff nurse leavers are altogether more dissatisfied. Nevertheless, if this outlook is associated with their departure from the present hospital it has not apparently encouraged them to separate from the NHS.

When we consider the division between male and female nurses the dominance of the latter among our respondents necessarily means that the effect of the predictors in their case corresponds closely to the picture for the sample as a whole. The main contrast rests in the enhanced position of grade among the subgroups. Interest therefore centres on the divergence of the predictors among male nurses from the overall pattern. Those variables which break out from the pack are notably short of domestic items and much more dominated by job attitudes. Educational attainment influences in the usual manner, while the type of living accommodation emerges for the first time, as those in the process of buying their own house display much higher stability. In addition, leavers are less likely to have many friends at work. This negative aspect is further reinforced by the much higher than usual association of several aspects of job satisfaction with turnover; with the direction indicating that those who are unhappy with their lot are more numerous among the leavers.

As one travels from the younger to the older nurses the strength of the predictors, both overall and individually, is sharply reduced. More, surprising still, there are several similarities in the hierarchy of effect across the two groups. Marriage and young children have a common impact as does the nurses' commitment to nursing. The main contrast rests with the extra effect of job features — the size of hospital and length of service — among the younger group.

Nevertheless there is sufficient evidence of contrasting effects between the subgroups within the nurse population to justify caution in drawing conclusions about the general impact of a specific determinant. Not that our chosen predictors of nursing turnover have been notably successful in their ascribed role, even after due allowance has been made for contrasts in the nurses' personal characteristics and in their work background.

If a breakdown of the population according to these key dimensions does not greatly improve the prediction of nursing turnover, what of the second possibility that we should categorise leavers according to their destination after moving from their current post? Those subjected to detailed analysis here are the leavers from the original set of questionnaire respondents. Detailed statistics for the whole group are illustrated in Table 4.3.[71]

The conclusion immediately suggested by these figures is that the attempt to predict the direction in which leavers travel meets with as little success as arose when our subject was turnover *per se*. The total amount of variation explained by all the determinants acting together is only 23 per cent. Moreover, there has been a slight convergence within the body of predictors so that the range of effect is narrowed, and no single factor stands so consistently head and shoulders above the remainder as previously occurred with the work intentions variable.

Table 4.3: Multiple Regression Statistics for Predictors of the Direction
of Nursing Turnover: All Leavers

Predictors	Simple r	R^2 change	Unstandardised regression coefficient	Standardised regression coefficient
Size of hospital	−.01	.000	−.04	−.06
Grade	.20	.04	.05	.06
Length of service	.17	.009	−.00	−.01
Hours worked	.17	.02	.10	.07
Future work intentions	.03	.00	−.04	−.06
Job satisfaction	−.06	.002	−.04	−.06
Supervision	−.08	.003	−.03	−.06
Communication	.12	.001	.05	.05
Pay and effort	.09	.00	−.00	−.00
Promotion prospects	.13	.01	.05	.10
Friends	−.12	.01	−.07	−.10
Other opportunities	.17	.01	.05	.08
Job commitment	−.03	.00	−.01	−.01
Sex	−.14	.03	−.16	−.15
Marital status	.34	.06	.29	.29
Children	.01	.02	−.23	−.17
Education	−.10	.00	−.02	−.02
Accommodation	−.30	.01	−.09	−.10

R^2 = 23%; Standard error = .46; N = 289

Despite this, several of the independent variables emerge as relatively
more influential than the remainder. At the top of the hierarchy is a
solid phalanx of domestic and personal characteristics: namely, marital
status, young children and the sex of the nurse. Females, the married,
and those without young children all opt with more intensity to leave
work. At a secondary level, those who have a favourable view of their
promotion prospects, who have few friends at their current workplace
and who are not owner-occupiers are relatively more prone to mobility
within the hospital network. A third rank comprises entirely work
variables. Staff nurses, full-timers and those who regard their chances
of finding another nursing job with some optimism all follow the
nursing trail which keeps them in the Health Service.

Within this overall structure the breakdown by grade reveals that the

Table 4.4: Multiple Regression Statistics for Predictors of the Direction of Nursing Turnover: by Grade of Leaver

Predictors	SEN		Staff Nurse		Ward Sister/ Charge Nurse	
	r	Src	r	Src	r	Src
Size of hospital	−.13	−.11	−.06	−.11	.11	.03
Length of service	.20	.20	.08	.02	.06	−.09
Hours worked	−.00	−.09	.27	.14	.16	.12
Future work intentions	−.09	−.25	.14	.02	−.12	−.05
Job satisfaction	−.03	−.12	−.03	−.00	−.07	−.04
Supervision	−.12	−.06	−.04	−.09	−.05	.00
Communication	−.06	−.09	.07	.01	.14	.05
Pay and effort	.24	.24	−.02	−.08	−.02	−.19
Promotion prospects	.16	.11	.17	.11	−.00	−.01
Friends	−.21	−.23	−.22	−.16	.18	.10
Other opportunities	.17	.01	05	.04	.25	.17
Job commitment	.14	.19	.01	−.01	−.26	−.26
Sex	−.03	−.21	−.12	−.10	−.29	−.21
Marital status	.20	.30	.37	.33	.32	.37
Children	−.03	−.03	.19	-.12	−.24	−.34
Education	−.16	−.02	−.02	.02	--.03	−.08
Accommodation	−.23	−.09	−.26	.03	−.32	−.17
R^2 =	.30		.21		.48	
Standard error	.48		.46		.40	
N =	51		126		68	

total variation explained spreads from 21 per cent for staff nurses, through 30 per cent for enrolled nurses, up to an impressive 48 per cent for ward sisters and charge nurses. This is a reversal of the amount of variation generated across the grades when there is a simple division between leavers and stayers. This is largely due to the relatively enhanced contribution of most predictors rather than an absence of certain variables from some groups and their obvious presence in others. Among enrolled nurses the first rank of predictors includes: the married, women, those with few friends at work, those satisfied with their pay, but who have otherwise few fond feelings towards nursing, despite their longer than average stay in the service — all these groups are more likely to give up work completely. In a similar fashion, ward sisters and charge nurses who quit the NHS demonstrate an association with being: married, without young children, female, pessimistic about finding another nursing post, owner-occupiers. In contrast with enrolled colleagues, however, this group of registered staff are satisfied with their career in nursing, but more disenchanted with the pay received compared to the effort they invest in their work. In between these two grades, marital status is the only variable which rates as a notable predictor of the direction in which staff nurses move. Yet once again it is the married ones who quit the service.

Although the predictors had not set off much variation among those over 35 years when the dependent variable was the simple dichotomy of left or stayed, the present separation by the direction followed is altogether more revealing. While the under-35s expel married nurses, and those with a rosy view of promotion prospects as most important in the association with leaving the NHS, the list of predictors influential among their elders is longer, and contains several predictors whose strength is most impressive. Thus, females, the married, those with few friends at work, who are disenchanted with job prospects, who rarely discuss their work with other nurses, who work full-time, in the larger hospitals, are all more likely to give up working.

While the general picture is of low impact on the amount of variation explained by these predictors when one examines the direction of mobility rather than turnover *per se*, there are several interesting points that arise out of this decomposition of the sample into smaller units. In specific groups, like senior registered staff, or older nurses, the predictors analysed constitute good statistical determinants. This success story rests essentially on the predictive effect of the personal and domestic circumstances of the nurses. Marital status, young children and sex of the nurse all assume a capacity to influence not hitherto demonstrated in such general or powerful terms. Given that the dependent variable splits between staying in the NHS and leaving — which basically means going into full-time domesticity — the greater power of most of these variables is not unanticipated. But job features and job attitudes are not submerged by this homely effect. Feelings of despair about promotion, or nursing vacancies elsewhere, especially among junior full-time staff, encourage a complete departure from nursing. Yet the lesser impact of the 'job satisfaction' syndrome among the predictors reinforces misgivings expressed earlier that the relationship between job satisfaction and staying in one's current hospital, or even the NHS, is far from straightforward. We know that a sizeable proportion of nurses leave the service prematurely, and if the prognostications of their speedy return are true, there is little justification for interpreting their loss as a reflection on nursing or their employer. Instead it is more a function of non-nursing conditions, or ambitions which if fulfilled restrict employment outside the home.

Just as job attitudes' influence is more complicated than much turnover research implies, the complex interaction of variables considerably confounds the analysis. At one level the influence of grade, for example, develops from the concentration of particular groups (the younger, single persons), and the favourable job features (better promotion possibilities, nursing posts elsewhere). And yet within the staff nurse grade there is in addition a group of older, part-time women with children who are less interested in mobility, and if they do leave, the direction chosen is often quite different to their younger colleagues. The implication is that the individual circumstances of those in nursing display considerable diversity, and that only after such internal differentiation has been allowed for will the prediction of nursing turnover — generally and in direction — be achieved with anything like reasonable statistical success.

Future Work Intentions: Some Further Analysis

Such is the pre-eminence of the nurses' expressed intention to leave or stay in the prediction of nursing turnover — and it appears even in the directional analysis — that we feel justified in considering the nature of its influence in more detail. This also facilitates comparison with other research on labour turnover since it has not been uncommon to employ 'intent to leave' as the measure of labour mobility, rather than actual departure. The presumption is that intent and actuality are very strongly related.[72] One American study reported that, from a sample of over 300 workers, 75 per cent of those who intended to stay in their current employment were still in post two years later, while 59 per cent who said they would leave actually did so. While the relationship as illustrated is statistically significant, a definite minority does not conform. The suggestion has been made that stability is more easily predicted than departure, but there is little detailed examination of the conditions which invalidate individuals' foretelling of the future. Moreover, there is a blasé assumption that those who forecast their departure (or retention) in fact leave (or stay) for the reasons which originally influenced their prognosis. Nor is there agreement about how far ahead individuals may reasonably be expected to know their whereabouts. In our case study, the period is one year, although Price and Bluedorn fix

Table 4.5: Relationship between Future Work Intentions and Actual
  Behaviour (per cent)

Intention	Stayed	Left	All
Definitely will leave	20.8 (4.2)	79.2 (49.4)	(15.2)
Uncertain	79.2 (48.3)	20.8 (39.4)	(46.2)
Definitely will stay	92.9 (7.1)	47.5 (11.2)	(38.6)
All	75.6	24.4	

on two years as more valid since the effect of intention to leave
increases with this extended viewpoint.[73] The inference is that nurses
either take a contrary interpretation of 'short term' to social scientists,
or intentions have been especially frustrated so that mobility has been
more difficult than envisaged.

The significance of the relationship between intent and action is
clearly illustrated from our own data in Table 4.5. Almost 80 per cent
óf those who forecast they will leave do exactly that; while even more
of the definite stayers — 92.9 per cent — keep to the prediction. This
confirms the greater accuracy with which stability can be determined.
It is interesting nevertheless to note that those nurses who report an
ambiguous or uncertain view congregate among the stayers to the tune
of 79.2 per cent. Much of the success of these figures stems from the
accuracy of the leaving intention in the early months after that
statement has been made. Conversely, of the intending stayers who
change their mind, just over one-half do not leave until the latter part
of the twelve-month period. A breakdown of these figures by grade,
hours and sex indicates further variation. In no instance is the basic
pattern undermined, but in some groups, such as males and senior
registered staff, the intending leavers are poorer forecasters, although
the overall correlation is maintained because the stayers are even less
likely to break with their plan.

Not only is the association between basic intention and practice
most significant, but perhaps as impressive, the reasons offered for
departure are stable over time.[74] Not surprisingly, those anticipating
their imminent departure are most likely to maintain their explanation.
Work-related reasons, which typically involve a movement to another
hospital post, are moderately more secure than non-work explanations.
This adds weight to the argument that domestic pressures are less easily
predicted, or fluctuate more than work factors. In comparison, the
nurses whose future is more problematic are notably less sure of the
reasons for their departure.

Further information on the stability of response is gleaned from the follow-up questionnaire sent to those who remained in post over the period of field-work. Again the nurses outlined their future work intentions. As Figure 4.3 demonstrates, however, there is little support for the conclusions in other research that an extension of our field-work by another twelve months will improve the predictive effect of the intent to leave variable. This assumes of course that intention and actual behaviour are as closely associated among the stayers as among the original population.

The use of intent to leave as an index of labour turnover also presumes that the predictors of this attitudinal forecast are the same as those of actual mobility. It will be remembered that intent to leave is by far the most powerful predictor of nursing turnover, and it is worth assessing this as a dependent variable in the same multiple regression analysis. Rather than begin our search for determinants from scratch we have taken the remaining variables from Table 4.1 which were used in the prediction of nursing turnover. These explain only a low level of variation in intent to leave. The new level is, however, matched by the inability of the predictors to induce much more variation with intent to leave as the measure of turnover. The demonstration that the same set of predictors are equally ineffectual across both dependent variables is a discouraging proposition with which to begin the comparison. More positively, the simple correlation figures across each of the predictors are impressively linked. In only a solitary instance — career satisfaction — is the direction of the association contradictory. Moreover, the level of the correlation coefficients differs by less than 0.1. A comparison of the standardised regression coefficients, where allowance is made for the intervention of other predictors, substantiates this pattern. This is a complete reversal of the conclusion from a study of American nurses that: 'The two measures of turnover yield substantially different results when testing the same causal model.'[75] Admittedly, there are several contrasts in the independent variables used, but there is sufficient overlap to allow for a direct comparison. Our main unease in offering unqualified support for the interchange of intent to leave and actual behaviour as measures of turnover is the low amount of explained variation in either of the dependent variables.

Summary Model of Nursing Turnover

In this section we attempt to draw together the results from the preceding discussion into a more succinct statement of the process of nursing turnover. Even if this entails an over-simplification of the influences at work, this shortcoming is countered by the advantage of

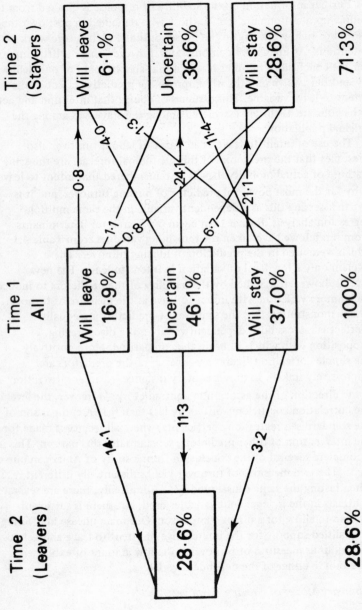

Figure 4.3: Relationship between Future Work Intentions and Behaviour at Time 1 and Time 2

specifying a clear structure within which nursing turnover occurs. The basic ingredients in our model of turnover among trained nurses concentrate into four areas. To start with, there is an important domestic syndrome which encompasses individual characteristics and personal relationships — such as sex, age, marital status, whether the individual has any young children, level of educational attainment, and to an extent, the type of accommodation lived in. Not that all of these variables fall evenly on individuals. The interaction of marital status and young children is of particular influence among female nurses, while their male colleagues are more affected by the accommodation and educational dimensions. There is clear support for the interpretation that being a woman with young children describes a range of constraints which do not affect a male with anything like the same force.

A second set of influences surrounds the occupational position held. The central feature is the grade of the nurse, but in addition it is valid to incorporate: hours worked, length of service and previous work record, and the size of the hospital in which currently placed. These variables encapsulate the pressures and possibilities at work, and their differential impact between groups of nurse. Junior registered nurses have particularly healthy prospects for movement to other nursing positions, but this ease of mobility interacts with the length of time spent in the employing hospital. The 'pure' force of these job features is, however, a mixture of occupational conditions and those outside circumstances which have helped place the individual nurse in that post. To be a part-time nurse suggests that the opportunities for mobility will be restricted, but in addition domestic and personal factors have already exerted their sway by locating individuals in a part-time post at the outset. Again, staff nurses have greater opportunities for movement, but this is reinforced by their generally lower age and single status, compared with other nurses. Indeed, among the older, married staff nurses, the evidence of stability in hospitals is noticeable, which is a reasonable indication of the manner in which domestic and personal conditions circumscribe the direct impact of job features. Not that the direction of influence is all one way, but the main tide springs from outside the hospital and nursing structure, or strongly mediates the directly occupational effect.

The third constellation of influences on nursing turnover encompasses the orientation to work espoused by nurses. It is widely accepted that the individual's job satisfaction is directly associated with retention or departure, but the support for this prediction is not apparent in this group of nursing employees. If there is any relationship between a

particular job attitude — such as the overall satisfaction with the
organisation of the hospital in which they work — this is countered by
negative opinions on job assignment, supervision and distributive justice.
The only clear-cut impact is the perceived ease of movement; so that
optimism breeds, or is related to, mobility. The failure of job
satisfaction variables to effect turnover stems from specific elements
and female employment patterns. The domination of nurse employment
vacancies by the NHS has been emphasised, but with this constraint of
trained nurses to stay within the service, there is some encouragement,
and considerable potential, to move between the constituent parts.
Inter-hospital mobility is then easily attributed to a commitment to,
and satisfaction with, nursing. In the same fashion, many of the female
nurses who are giving up work voice few grievances with their
profession or their employer since the reasons for their departure are
essentially domestic or related to their family circumstances.
Furthermore, many of these departures are not 'final', since a large
proportion of these leavers intend to return to nursing when
circumstances permit. In consequence, the mobile group contains many
nurses who are not noticeably dissatisfied with their job. Nevertheless,
it is rather more likely that those who express dissatisfaction will not
loom large among the stayers. If satisfaction does not guarantee staying
in one's current post, dissatisfaction is more associated with mobility.
Nevertheless, there remains within nursing a disenchanted minority who
decide to endure their discomfort, or perhaps have no option.

One attitude, which separates itself from the remainder, both for
its concentration on the future as well as for its association with
turnover among nurses, is the individuals' own prediction of their
behaviour. To an extent, this prediction will derive from domestic and
occupational features, as well as attitudes about current conditions at
work. But as with the other connecting links between the main areas of
influence, the relationship is rarely simple or direct. The central
difficulty in the inclusion of this forecast within any model of nursing
turnover hinges upon its failure to enumerate those conditions which
give rise to turnover — unless one reduces the explanation to the wholly
unacceptable equation: intent to leave 'causes' departure. It is, however,
legitimate to emphasise that the intent to stay or leave interacts both
with nurses' job attitudes, and with domestic factors, in a way which
highlights the possibility for a change in intention to occur. This returns
the discussion to those writers who perceive turnover as the progressive
movement towards a position of fixity within an organisation. The
'settledness' of the connection which nurses have with a particular

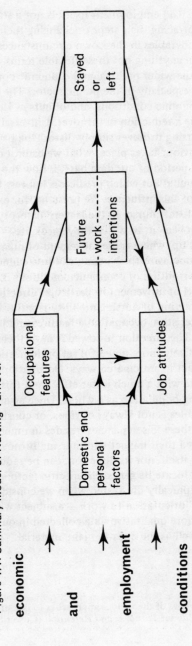

Figure 4.4: Summary Model of Nursing Turnover

economic

and

employment

conditions

hospital, or with paid employment itself, is not a state at which they arrive without retracing their steps or changing their minds. There are too many imponderables in their own circumstances as well as in nursing to talk in anything but these flexible terms. This raises a further question about the wider political and economic constraints upon those in employment, especially in the public sector. The immediate impact of depressed economic conditions, and of cuts in Health Service spending, include a reduction in turnover. Universal models of the predictors of nursing turnover simply distort the backdrop against which such behaviour takes place. What we cannot demonstrate, with the limited time period of our data base, is how the decline/increase in nurse mobility will affect which predictors impress themselves, and the scope and level of this influence. We presume, for example, that the predominance of staff nurses in the leavers' category will be diminished as the type of movement in which they specialise — that is, between hospitals — dries up; whereas the movement of many female nurses into domesticity to look after their young children cannot be avoided, or put off. The intervention of economic conditions is likely to be more acute on the level of movement in particular directions. More generally, however, the direction of nursing mobility is influenced by domestic/ personal characteristics, occupational features and job attitudes as is turnover *per se.* The direction followed is nevertheless most subject to a wider and relatively more powerful set of domestic and personal variables which act in anticipated ways. Occupational features, and job attitudes, operate with a much lesser effect and this conclusion applies across the nursing population as a whole. Once again, the influence of these work variables is not always obvious, or consistent, but the explanation for these 'discrepancies' resides in much the same reasons as earlier disguised their impact with nursing turnover. Quite simply, neither turnover itself, nor its direction, can be reduced to simple equations which locate its genesis in specific factors. The force of this conclusion is graphically illustrated when we consider in more detail the nature of nurses' orientation to work — a subject which demands analysis of the more qualitative data collected in our personal interviews with nurses, as well as the questionnaire material.

Notes

1. Excellent reviews of the various approaches to labour turnover include B. Pettman (ed.), *Labour Turnover and Retention* (Gower Press, London, 1975);

J.M. Cousins, 'Values and Value in the Labour Market', Working Papers in Sociology, no.9, University of Durham, undated, J. Price, *The Study of Turnover* (Ames, Iowa State University Press, 1977).

2. For further exposition of the labour market account see J.R. Hicks, *The Theory of Wages* (Macmillan, London, 1932); C. Myers, 'Labour Market Theory and Empirical Research' in J. Dunlop (ed.), *The Theory of Wage Determination* (Macmillan, London, 1957), ch.20.

3. H. Lind, 'Internal Migration in Britain' in J.A. Jackson (ed.), *Migration* (Cambridge University Press, Cambridge, 1969), ch.4.

4. H. Makower, J. Marshak and H. Robinson, 'Studies in the Mobility of Labour: Analysis for Great Britain: Part II', *Oxford Economic Papers*, no.4 (1940), pp.59-60.

5. A. Marshall, *Principles of Economics*, 3rd edn. (Macmillan, London, 1895), p.638.

6. L.G. Reynolds, *The Structure of Labour Markets* (Harper, New York. 1951), pp.369-72.

7. Myers, 'Labour Market Theory and Empirical Research', p.321.

8. Ibid., pp.325-6.

9. Lind, 'Internal Migration in Britain', p.77.

10. C. Kerr, 'The Balkanisation of Labour Markets' in E.W. Bakke (ed.), *Labour Mobility and Economic Opportunity* (Cambridge, Mass., MIT Press, 1954).

11. D. Robinson, *Wage Drift, Fringe Benefits and Manpower Distribution* (OECD, Paris, 1968), p.66.

12. Kerr, 'The Balkanisation of Labour Markets'.

13. Robinson, *Wage Drift, Fringe Benefits and Manpower Distribution*, p.66

14. Ibid., p.88.

15. D. Mackay, D. Boddy, J. Brack, J. Diack and N. Jones, *Labour Markets under Different Employment Conditions* (Allen and Unwin, London 1971).

16. R.G. Brown and R. Stones, *The Male Nurse*, Occasional Papers on Social Administration, no.52 (Bell, London, 1973).

17. J.G. March and H.A. Simon, *Organisations* (Wiley, New York, 1958), ch.4,

18. H. Behrend, 'Absence and Labour Turnover in a Changing Economic Climate', *Occupational Psychology*, vol.27 (1955), p.79; see also B. Pettman, *Labour Turnover and Retention*, ch.2.

19. Reported in Pettman, 'External and Personal Determinants of Labour Turnover', pp.36-7; T. Moreton, 'Towards a Model of Labour Turnover and Job Choice', *Personnel Review*, vol.3 (1974), pp.12-22.

20. Myers, 'Labour Market Theory and Empirical Research', p.320.

21. W.M. Williams (ed.), *Occupational Choice* (Allen and Unwin, London, 1974).

22. G. Mercer and D.J.C. Forsyth, 'Some Aspects of Recruitment to School Teaching', *British Journal of Educational Studies*, vol.XXIII (1975), pp.58-77.

23. Reynolds, *The Structure of Labour Markets*, p.85.

24. Ibid., p.85.

25. A first-rate review of the literature is contained in J. MacGuire, *Threshold to Nursing*, Occasional Papers on Social Administration, no.30 (Bell, London. 1969), p.39.

26. Ibid., pp.39-42.

27. Ibid., pp.39-42; Brown and Stones, *The Male Nurse*.

28. G. Palmer, *The Reluctant Job Changer* (University of Pennsylvania, Phil., 1962).

29. M. Mann, *Workers on the Move* (Cambridge University Press, Cambridge, 1973), ch.3.

30. M. Jefferys, *Mobility in the Labour Market* (Routledge and Kegan Paul, London, 1964), p.123.

31. V. Olesen and E. Whittaker, *The Silent Dialogue* (Jossey-Bass, Pennsylvania, 1968), pp.296-7.

32. Jefferys, *Mobility in the Labour Market*, p.130.

33. C. Thomas, 'The Mobility of Labour in Great Britain', *Occupational Psychology*, vol.27 (1953), pp.215-20.

34. March and Simon, *Organisations;* Price, *The Study of Turnover* B. Pettman, 'Some Factors Influencing Labour Turnover: a Review of Research Literature', *Industrial Relations*, vol.4 (1973), pp.43-61.

35. Reynolds, *The Structure of Labour Markets;* March and Simon, *Organisations*, ch.4.

36. M. Weir (ed.), *Job Satisfaction* (Fontana, Glasgow, 1976).

37. March and Simon, *Organisations*, pp.94-5. The discussion centres on this book, and the complementary review by Pettman, 'Some Factors Influencing Labour Turnover'.

38. March and Simon, *Organisations*, p.95.

39. We refer henceforward to questions in the first-wave questionnaire contained in the Appendix Qs. 11, 19, 20, 32, 33.

40. March and Simon, *Organisations*, p.95.

41. E. Fleishman and E. Harris, 'Patterns of Leadership Behaviour related to Employee Grievances and Turnover', *Personnel Psychology*, vol 15 (1962), pp.43-56; R. Blauner, *Alienation and Freedom* (Chicago University Press, Chicago, 1964); Price, *The Study of Turnover*. The relevant questions in our study are nos. 11, 16, 17. 20.

42. March and Simon, *Organisations*, pp.95-6; J. Greystoke, G. Thomason and T. Murphy, 'Labour Turnover Surveys', *Personnel Management*, vol.34 (1952), pp.158-65.

43. Price, *The Study of Turnover*; Qs. 25, 26, 27, 28, 29.

44. March and Simon, *Organisations*, p.96; Q. 45.

45. Ibid., p.97; Q. 29.

46. Pettman, 'Some Factors Influencing Labour Turnover'.

47. March and Simon, *Organisations*, p.97; Qs. 6, 8.

48. P.F. Brissenden and E. Frankel, *Labour Turnover in Industry: a Statistical Analysis* (Macmillan, New York, 1922); J.M. Hill, *The Seafaring Career: a Study of the Forces Affecting Joining, Serving and Leaving the Merchant Navy* (Tavistock Institute, London, 1972).

49. March and Simon, *Organisations*, p.98.

50. G.S. Bain, *The Growth of White Collar Unionism* (Oxford University Press Oxford, 1970).

51. E. Mayo and G. Lombard, *Teamwork and Labour Turnover in the Aircraft Industry in Southern California*, Business Research Studies, no.32 (Harvard Graduate School of Business Administration, Cambridge, Mass., 1944).

52. Q.7.

53. March and Simon, *Organisations*, p.99; Greystoke *et al.*, 'Labour Turnover Surveys'; G. Ingham, *Size of Industrial Organisation and Worker Behaviour* (Cambridge University Press, Cambridge, 1970).

54. March and Simon, *Organisations*, p.100; Qs. 30, 31, 4, 7.

55. Greystoke *et al.*, 'Labour Turnover Surveys'; B. Pettman, *Womanpower: an Underutilised Resource* (MCB Monographs, Bradford, 1977), pp.16-20; Q. 39.

56. Q. 40.

57. March and Simon, *Organisations*, pp.101-2; Jefferys, *Mobility in the Labour Market*; A. Harris, *Labour Mobility in Great Britain* (Government Social Survey, London, 1964); Q. 41.

58. Mann, *Workers on the Move*; March and Simon, *Organisations*, p.102; C. Bell, *Middle Class Families* (Routledge and Kegan Paul, London, 1969); Qs. 40, 41.

59. Q. 40.

60. Qs. 42, 43.

61. March and Simon, *Organisations*, p.102, Price, *The Study of Turnover*, Q. 4.

62. March and Simon, *Organisations*, pp.103-6; Qs. 19, 30, 31, 33, 38.

63. March and Simon, *Organisations*, p.105.

64. Qs. 11, 34, 46, 47, 49.

65. J. Price and A. Bluedorn, 'Test of a Causal Model of Organisational Turnover', unpublished paper, Department of Sociology, University of Iowa, 1977.

66. J. Sonquist, *Multivariate Model Building* (University of Michigan, Ann Arbor, 1970).

67. G. Mercer and C. Mould, *An Investigation into the Level and Character of Labour Turnover amongst Trained Nurses*, Report for the DHSS (University of Leeds, 1976).

68. The reader should note that not all of the final set of predictors appear in each regression run reported here. The reason quite simply is that in some instances their effect on the dependent variable was so small that their inclusion is irrelevant.

69. The values of the final list variables employed in the multiple regression analysis are as follows:
(a) Nursing turnover: stayed (0); left (1).
(b) Size of hospital: large (1); medium (2); small (3).
(c) Grade: staff nurse (1); SEN (2); ward sister/charge nurse (3); SSEN (4).
(d) Length of service: under 6 months (0.25); 6 months to 1 year (0.75); 1 to 2 years (1.5); 2 to 3 years (2.5); 3 to 4 years (3.5); 4 to 5 years (4.5); 5 to 10 years (7.5); 10 to 15 years (12.5); 15 to 20 years (17.5); 20 to 25 years (22.5); 25 to 30 years (27.5).
(e) Hours worked: full-time (1); part-time (2).
(f) Ward specialism: maternity (1); other specialism (2); general medical and surgical (3); several/nights (4).
(g) Shift; lates, earlies or combination (1); nights (2).
(h) Number of hospitals worked at: one (1); two (2); three (3); four or more (4).
(i) Intent to leave/future work intentions: definitely will leave (1); slight chance of leaving/situation is uncertain (2); definitely will not leave (3).
(j) Sex: female (1); male (2).
(k) Marital status: single (1); married/divorced/widowed (2).
(l) Any young children: none (0); yes (1).
(m) Age: 20 to 24 years (1); 25 to 29 years (2); 30 to 34 years (3); 35 to 39 years (4); 40 to 44 years (5); 45 to 49 years (6); 50 years + (7).
(n) Educational attainment: passed 'O' levels (1); no 'O' levels (0).
(o) Living accommodation: own/buying a house (1); living with relatives (2); in rented accommodation (3).
(p) Job satisfaction index: constructed from items whether nursing is: dull/exciting, taken for granted/respected, routine/varied, regimented/free of restrictions: negative view (3); in-between (2); positive (1).
(q) Friends at work: none (0); one or two (1); three or more (2).
(r) Satisfaction with hospital organisation: satisfied (1); ambivalent (2); dissatisfied (3).
(s) Extent of supervision: supervisor not amenable to persuasion (3); in-between (2); amenable to persuasion (1).

(t) Work communication: none (0); yes (1).
(u) Pay-effort distributive justice: pay is: bad (1); about right (2); good (3).
(v) Promotion prospects: good (1); about right (2); bad (3).
(w) Other nursing opportunities: easy (1); not sure (2); difficult (3).
(x) Career satisfaction: yes (1); ambivalent (2); no (3).

70. J. Price and A. Bluedorn, 'Intent to Leave as a Measure of Turnover', unpublished paper, Department of Sociology, University of Iowa, 1977; T.W. Mangione, 'Turnover — Some Psychological and Demographic Correlates' in R. Quinn and T. Mangione (eds.), *The 1969-1970 Survey of Working Conditions* (Survey Research Centre, University of Michigan, 1973).

71. In this case the values of the dependent variable are as follows: moved to another post in the NHS (1); moved out of the NHS/work (2).

72. Price and Bluedorn, 'Intent to Leave as a Measure of Turnover', Mangione, 'Turnover'.

73. Price and Bluedorn, 'Intent to Leave as a Measure of Turnover'.

74. The reasons for leaving at time 1 are taken from the first-wave questionnaire, while the time 2 responses derive from the data collection over the period of our field-work with leavers.

75. Price and Bluedorn 'Intent to Leave as a Measure of Turnover', p.28.

5 WORK, NURSING AND LABOUR TURNOVER

We have argued, in previous chapters, that to understand labour turnover it must be placed within the wider context of the orientation to work. The search is not for an explanation of why people work, but why nursing has been chosen, and yet more specifically, what has prompted recruitment to, and retention in, the current hospital post. The empirical translation of this orientation has not been without considerable wrangling and trenchant polemics.[1] A critic offers a synopsis of the 'social action' approach:

> People are asked, for example, why they chose a particular work situation, why they remained and what features of the job they value. From their answers ideas about orientation to work are derived and then categorised according to some variation on the instrumental/expressive theme. From this it is ascertained whether the respondents see work as primarily a source of extrinsic or intrinsic rewards.[2]

The obvious inference is that the same orientation explains entry, as well as exit, from employment. The criticism levelled against this view is that those factors which bring individuals into a specific job are not necessarily the same as those which keep them there, let alone those which take them away from that employment.[3] It is obligatory then to offer a brief|résumé of the theoretical underbrush to this debate before we proceed to discuss the specific case of nurses and nursing.

In so far as people typically regard work as the source of general and specific 'wants', and a central social reference point in their lives, the presumption is that individuals express satisfaction to the extent that experience matches expectations. Traditionally, individual work behaviour is reducible to rational self-interest. This is essentially the assumption on which F.W. Taylor developed his recipe for scientific management and increased industrial profitability.[4] Since then, opinion has progressed towards a contrary conclusion that employees are 'not self-interested individuals but persons with attitudes and feelings'.[5] This 'human relations' standpoint sees workers' behaviour as essentially conditioned by their role and status in a group. Modern factory life threatened 'dehumanisation'. 'Worker motivation, far from

being concerned exclusively with the maximisation of monetary
rewards, was essentially emotional, related more to the norms of the
work group and the working environment than to the cost of living
index.'[6] More contemporary writers in this tradition have extended
this formula into a considerable array of psychological needs and
aspirations. Most of the inspiration behind this development has been
the work of Maslow, and the subsequent refinements introduced by
Herzberg.[7] In Maslow's scheme, people are motivated by a hierarchy
of needs, which start with basic physiological wants, and stretch
through into 'higher' drives for self-fulfilment. In Herzberg's
'motivation-hygiene' theory individuals have two basic needs: one set
which demands the avoidance of deprivation, and a second group,
which involves the realisation of individuals' full potential. Maslow
presumes that the hierarchy operates so that once particular needs are
satisfied, workers will turn elsewhere for 'self-actualisation'. In
empirical studies, Herzberg attempts to specify in detail those job
context factors which inhibit dissatisfaction. He concentrates upon
pay and working conditions. If these are regarded as inadequate the
consequent disenchantment will, amongst other things, stimulate
labour turnover. Highly positive feelings towards work arise when job
content factors, such as the need for a challenge, recognition and
self-esteem, are gratified. In those circumstances a high level of labour
stability is anticipated.

At this point, there is an overlap between the psychological and
some sociological approaches. Blauner, for example, indicates that
'When work provides opportunities for control, creativity, and
challenge — when, in a word, it is self-expressive and enhances an
individual's unique potentialities — then it contributes to the worker's
sense of self-respect and dignity.'[8] Blauner's focus is upon the level and
character of workers' alienation, which he describes as 'a general
syndrome made up of a number of different objective conditions and
subjective feeling-states'.[9] His thesis is that these comprise:
powerlessness, over control of the work process, its speed and methods;
meaninglessness, over the perceived lack of purpose in the tasks done,
or its products; isolation, from the rest of the work-force; and self-
estrangement, because one's work fails to provide any real sense of
identity.[10] What Blauner stresses is the manner in which such alienation
is a function of the technology in the workplace. Despite the
increasingly technological factor in modern medicine and nursing, and
the claims that patient care at times resembles a factory production line,
nursing conditions are some distance from those in manufacturing

industry. Not that alienation is simply technologically determined, for the complex interaction between modern production processes and worker behaviour and attitudes is a subject which has provoked considerable dispute.[11] In car assembly plants it has been demonstrated how 'instrumentalism' dominates in certain technologies where the workers enjoy little scope for job participation or satisfaction. They acquire a calculative attitude where financial rewards and incentives are central. It is not that workers are anaesthetised from unattractive work by high pay, but more significantly it is offset to a degree by the attempt to achieve desired ends in the non-work world.[12] In this interpretation, the lack of 'full' material rewards sets off a chain reaction — which includes increased departures. However, in many occupations the orientation to work is not easily reduced to a single characteristic. In nursing there is little accent on economic motives; instead interpersonal or relational needs, and the less tangible intrinsic rewards are more to the fore.[13] The exact balance of these aspects is much disputed, but as sociologists have veered towards labelling manual workers as more instrumental, their non-manual counterparts supposedly regard work as their 'central life interest'. For example, Dubin's American manual worker sample expressed a clear preference for the non-work world, where relationships and activities were rated more satisfying and rewarding. Of particular interest for our research, therefore, is the follow-up study conducted by Orzack among a sample of US nurses.[14] While 24 per cent of manual workers offered responses which signified that their central life interest lay at work, the corresponding percentage among nurses was 79 per cent. Nurses then rank as typical of other professional and higher-status occupational groups in that they enjoy 'emotionally significant experiences or social relationships' at work, which makes it the prime 'source of self-realisation'.[15]

Certainly nursing is widely regarded as an occupation which provides job satisfaction, both by its practitioners and the community in general.[16] The emphasis is on intrinsic qualities, although it is not too jaundiced a view to argue that with the level of economic rewards in the profession, there is little alternative but to highlight this aspect. Nursing is lauded for its social relationships and close contacts with colleagues and patients. The popular stereotype is of a group dedicated to 'tender, loving care', but there are those in nursing circles who deny that the 'Florence' ideal is predominant among contemporary nurses. In the most referenced categorisation, Habenstein and Christ identify three main types of nurse: the professionaliser, the traditionaliser and the utiliser.[17] The first is preoccupied with nursing knowledge, and with curing diseases rather than caring for the patient in the wider sense. The more traditional nurse is the upholder of TLC, and the deferential handmaiden of medical knowledge and practitioners. The utiliser nurse eschews both these orientations. Instead,

> She is the prototype of the nurse as a piece rate worker, a low level, non-professional, organisational employee who simply does her job. She 'utilises' the medical context for her own outside interests. Developing and using a distinctive body of knowledge has little appeal for her.[18]

The main split in terms of our discussion is between the first two types which represent the overtly self-actualisation approach. In so far as these attitudinal constellations exist among nurses, they imply contrasting interpretations of nursing turnover. In the main, the utilisers quit nursing if their economic demands are not reasonably satisfied. In contrast, professionalisers and traditionalisers are presumed more wedded to nursing *per se*, although there is an expectation of professionalisers that they will move more between hospitals in their endeavour to advance in the nursing hierarchy. The pitfall behind this schema is that it ignores the broader circumstances of nurses, which may circumscribe the ease of mobility, however much it is desired.

Recruitment to Nursing

The orientation to nursing is first traced to the point of recruitment. Those studies which have examined occupational choice retrospectively have tended to become stuck in the gloriously unspecific response 'I've always wanted to' when the question is posed, 'Why nursing?' Even if valid, one wonders what it was about nursing which was so attractive. Or did they drift into the field without careful forethought, seeing it as just another job? There is good reason to believe that a lot of girls consider becoming a nurse. This emerges from several studies of adolescents.[19] Our questioning of nurses labours under the difficulty that the respondents' memory is liable to disappear, or to be reconstituted — always presuming that the reasons could ever be properly articulated. Nevertheless, the replies offered by our interviewees fit into several well defined categories.

The first group expresses the feeling that 'it was something I always wanted to do,' or that 'I always fancied it.'[20] These responses are restricted to women and have their genesis way back in childhood. 'As a young girl, I always dressed up as a nurse and it was always at the back of my mind.' Or else there was someone in the family with a nursing connection, or perhaps they, or a close relative, had been in hospital when young. The dominant impression is that as girls they had been smitten with the nursing bug; partly because of the supposed glamour, the uniform, the presumed life and death atmosphere and so forth, but also because few, if any, occupational alternatives were available, or seriously considered. Direct references to the traditional function of caring for the sick barely rate a mention.

The main alternative to the 'childhood ambition' replies — offered by approximately one-third of all those interviewed — stems from those who only decide to nurse after they have tried some other employment position. To this group, the initial attraction of nursing is cast in basic, instrumental terms. As one charge nurse explained, 'It was the most secure job around, and our factory looked as if it was about to close down.' Since almost 60 per cent of nurses have accumulated some non-nursing work experience, this suggests a solid foundation of calculative interest at the point of entry to nursing, although its continued expression is less evident. This is particularly true of male nurses, who at entry to the profession are on average several years older than their female counterparts in the same grade. More typically, they were drawn hesitantly into nursing, and often did consider this alternative until they finally took the plunge. In their choice, male nurses outline their instrumental intentions. If the rate of pay as such is not the primary attraction, it is the security and good prospects for advancement. According to one male nurse, 'I left teaching because nursing prospects were better. . .wasn't committed to nursing and patient care at that time but it's gradually developed.' That nursing is an unusual path for men to tread is often raised by male nurses themselves. It was a mystery to one charge nurse how he came to join the Health Service, 'Can't imagine, hated it,. . .I still have a complex about being called a nurse. . .only kept going because I couldn't be bothered looking for something else.'

The more instrumental orientation also varies between the grades. Enrolled staff are the most likely to have had previous employment and a significant proportion of these had worked in manual jobs, where they had immediate contact with 'the money is why we're here' attitude — if what other studies report is accurate. As a result, they bring an experience, and a set of attitudes, to nursing which are not typical of professionals.

Our interviewees were also asked why they chose their first hospital.

The responses divide in two. The first, and largest, category includes replies couched in pragmatic terms. Either the hospital was conveniently close to where the nurse was living, or accommodation was available with relatives. The second group of replies describe a positive, 'pull' effect. For some the hospital offered a good training, or it had a high reputation generally.[21] A similar pattern emerges in the choice of a fresh hospital after qualification. Again, the more notable proportion gravitate to a hospital because of its location above all else. Convenience for living at home is supplemented by closeness to friends, while movements because of a shift in their spouses' job become more prominent. To the particular group of female nurses with heavy family responsibilities, close proximity of work, or within easy travelling distance, are especially important. Again, for others there is the opportunity to move not just anywhere but to transfer to a town or area which is regarded as a pleasant place to live. If such geographical mobility can incorporate a good post at a reputable hospital, then so much the better. For a minority, the hospital's reputation as a place to nurse outweighs all else, 'Probably because it's the most talked about in Leeds. You can't go any higher. It's always understood that you get the best of everything.' This professional orientation is complemented by those nurses whose move is linked to their promotion, although the stimulus is as likely to be the extra salary. A small group do definitely leave in order to work the better-paid night shift, but such instrumental motives rarely surface in inter-hospital mobility. More often nurses anticipate that their new hospital will provide better working conditions than the present institution, but this move is as much due to the push of the latter as any clear view of life in the new environment.

From this brief inspection the world of nursing recruitment appears as a melting pot of all manner of work, social and personal interests. Occupational choice has occurred without real reflection on the alternatives — scarce though these perhaps are — or indeed of the pros or cons of nursing. Once a fully fledged nurse, however, the range of occupational alternatives narrows and practical outside interests increasingly assert themselves.

Job Satisfaction in Nursing

The difficulties involved in specifying the nature of job satisfaction, let alone the factors conducive to its variation, are legion.[22] No approach is without its critics. In this, we accept that it is important to identify whether trained nursing staff lay more emphasis on extrinsic, job contextual, or intrinsic, job content features. Together these encompass satisfaction with rewards (distributive justice) across both pay and promotion prospects, in relation to the effort injected into one's work generally and in contrast to other workers. Working conditions also cover the physical environment − the dirt, noise and so forth − as well as the physical and mental demands of the work tasks. Relational expectations derive from recognition of one's contribution, the establishment of emotional ties with one's workmates, and equitable treatment by supervisors. The extent of supervision extends into the level of autonomy and responsibility experienced. The aim is work that is varied, controlled by the individual, meaningful and an obvious value and purpose. In sum, it should be creative, challenging and role-appropriate. [23]

In our experience, the bland request for information on whether nurses are satisfied with their work elicits a generally positive response. Careful questioning on the features of work which the nurses deem attractive generates more explicit comment. 'Seeing a patient come in poorly and go out better.' 'Seeing patients who are badly burned, who you think will never walk again, gradually get better, and then going walking out through the door.' Nurses feel themselves to be an integral part of a crucial social activity, which contributes in a fundamental sense to individual well-being. 'Caring for someone' not only denotes a work role but also spells out a highly regarded self-image. Most nurses are keen to affirm that they are 'doing something worthwhile, that people appreciate'. The respect which they feel that nursing enjoys in the community encourages many to insist that 'it's not just another job.'

Equally important, nurses can ascribe an obvious meaning to their work − that is, to nursing *per se*. It is relevant to people's needs. It has a tangible effect, and perhaps dramatically so. Nurses have an identity in people's minds. This may flow from aiding the recovery of a desperately ill person, to assistance bringing a child into the world, to the less 'glamorous' caring for old people or psychiatric patients. Much of this satisfaction is connected to a very traditionalist orientation. 'Well, every delivery is different. The mums think they're marvellous, you feel so elated. They've done it all. You've done nothing really. It's lovely to see the mums and husbands so happy.' Such an easy identification of the end product of one's labours is not evenly spread through nursing. In other areas, death is more frequent, or recovery far more long-term or indefinite, but these situations provide more than enough scope for nurses to practise their craft and care for the patients.

A strong emphasis is laid on the absence of 'petty' restrictions and excessive supervision. Nurses are much attached to the prospect of doing their work, at their own speed, or in their own way. Such possibilities are restricted to senior registered staff. 'I enjoy running my own ward, and having my own staff. I enjoy being able to develop my own ideas. I have left behind the day-to-day dull work I used to do.' Nurses like that ward sister feel they have acquired a new sense of importance within the hospital hierarchy. They are entrusted with the responsibility of carrying out the instructions of consultants, or they find themselves passing on their knowledge to learners. Yet not even they are completely freed of supervisors, and ward sisters and charge nurses cherish the freedom from an overbearing No. 7 breathing down their neck all the time. To avoid all-enveloping rules and regulations or an over-present supervisor is a central goal, whatever their grade. Enrolled nurses are particularly resentful of what they see as over-regimentation by registered nurses, and look forward to the opportunities which occasionally come their way — generally fortuitously, because of staff shortages. As one enrolled nurse proclaimed, 'I then run this clinic virtually single handed. . .can do what I want. . .that's the way I like it.' Some argue that this devolution of responsibility, and the diminution of bureaucratically regulated task work, makes for a much improved atmosphere on the ward. Indeed when comparisons are made with other wards or units within the hospital, the freedom from 'excessive and petty restrictions' by supervisors is one of the main factors why a ward is ranked as a more attractive place to work.

It is noticeable that nurses accentuate the specific opportunities for caring in their own specialism. This is not unlinked to an awareness that they are not part of the life-and-death hospital drama enacted in TV serials, and nurses keenly emphasise the 'other world' of nursing. Most especially, work away from the acute divisions appeals because of its more relaxed atmosphere. This allows nurses to establish a close rapport with their patients, as well as their fellow nurses. 'You've got time to talk to your patients and get to know them,' reported an SEN on a geriatric rehabilitation unit. In like manner a staff nurse on a dermatology ward described the benefits of informality: 'There's all sorts of things that patients will tell you in general conversation that might give a clue as to why their condition has just broke out after six years.' There is, in other words, scope for judgement and initiative.

There is also a longing to have some variety in their work. While a certain amount of routine and discipline is accepted as necessary — especially in acute divisions — nurses express satisfaction if they have

the chance to 'do their own thing'. This might seem an ever-present
reality when every patient is different. Nevertheless what to an outsider
is manifest is frequently submerged within hospitals by an obsessive
ward routine which translates patients into a specific number of work
tasks. More positively, the variety demanded will bring in its train new
challenges. It is the very opposite of the monotony of the assembly line
in the factory. 'It's the variation. . .it's not routine. . .it's exhilarating
really because you don't know what's going to come in the door next.'
Or as a ward sister commented, 'Every time you go on the ward
something different happens.'

The personal contact and camaraderie is another facet of hospital
life which nurses regularly mention. On one level, they have in mind
the contact with patients. At another level it is friendship with
colleagues. This feeling is quite general, although female nurses who
have returned after a break to look after their family rate this aspect
particularly highly. To them, the personal contact provided by nursing
is a blessed release from the more solitary domestic routine. 'But for
nursing, I would have turned into a vegetable.' These individuals do not
reject family life, but they are worried that without other work they
are trapped in a privatised existence. Their aim is a variety of interests.

References are also made, though not in the same volume, to the
working conditions of the nurse. Few, of their own volition, refer
favourably (or disparagingly) to the physical conditions of work. Lack
of noise, heat, danger and so forth are treated as 'givens'. Even in 1975,
and just after the Halsbury increases, few offer complimentary remarks
about the scale of remuneration.[24] No one could say that nurses are
imbued with instrumentalism, but many more (registered staff) mention
the security that good promotion prospects instil. Nurses as a whole are
rather more convinced that they will always be able to find a job as a
nurse. This is of obvious importance to those who envisage only a
short-term break and aim to return to the same job later on. Even the
severe curtailment in job vacancies in recent years has barely dimmed
their optimism. Another source of reassurance to many of the current
work-force is the flexibility in hours of work. Indeed this encourages
the belief among intending leavers that there are few obstacles to their
return.

In their replies trained staff concentrate on the positive job content
in nursing. They focus on the nature of the service provided, its value
and purpose — both in terms of community acceptance and their own
self-fulfilment. The responses are evenly balanced between the
professional and traditional, and often this mixture emerges in

individual nurses. More distinctly, nurses stand well apart from those answers which fit the category of the utiliser nurse.

The other side of the coin is the nurses' representation of the sources of dissatisfaction in their work. With few exceptions, the unacceptable features of nursing are a mirror image of those areas which generate positive feelings. Except that one attitude is not contradicted. This is the assertion that nursing is a worthy social activity. The benefits of nursing care and the value of the nursing service are highly regarded, although there is dispute about whether society's financial response reflects this esteem. As a rule nursing pay tends to follow other settlements, and the satisfaction with monetary rewards therefore much depends on the time when interviews are conducted. Immediately prior to our field-work there had been some recovery of nursing remuneration against other groups, and hardly any expressed intense displeasure with their pay. Similarly, few decried their working conditions. The main bone of contention focused on the opportunities for promotion provided by the NHS, or their particular hospital. In some specialisms the prospects were felt very poor. 'It's so frustrating, there's little chance of promotion here (in theatre nursing) as there's so many qualified staff above me.' Part of this disaffection arises because some nurses are able to move elsewhere with relative ease to obtain promotion. Enrolled staff are particularly frustrated by their career stagnation, and by what this entails in the delegation of responsibility on the ward. They fret that their main hope for promotion to senior positions is to remain at the same hospital, and yet during this time they may find themselves supervised by student nurses. Not unexpectedly, staff nurses are least likely to make disparaging comments about the promotion prospects, although with the recent diminution of movement criticism has increased. A further elevation up the hierarchy for ward sisters and charge nurses is more problematic. After the relative spate of promotion into administrative posts following the reorganisation of the nursing structure and the Health Service itself, the number of vacancies has contracted. In consequence, some from the senior ward sister ranks feel, 'stuck in the same grade' longer than they envisaged, or quite simply have had enough of 'doing the same old things'. At the same time, there is displeasure with the career structure because the main road for advancement leads out of the clinical situation, or away from 'real nursing'. While some are rationalising their inertia, this view echoes the typical descriptions of what nursing is all about. Moreover, the antagonism often directed towards nursing administrators means that to join them is tantamount to the 'gamekeeper turning poacher'. Nevertheless, the higher pay structure is an attractive compensation.

Another area of adverse comment was the inability to nurse properly because of the shortage of staff, or the reliance on learners. 'We've just lost an auxiliary on this ward and the work load is getting too much.' While a ward sister on an Accident Unit commented that the combination of increasingly long hours and too few staff was making work a nightmare, 'There's a constant threat of emergency and catastrophe. . .no time for meal breaks which is bound to affect reactions and temper.' The feelings expressed indicate a fear that nurses are being exploited, and that their traditional dedication is being taken for granted.

There is also internal dissension among trained staff. It is not merely that nurses feel themselves put upon by the public, or the hospital authorities, but their treatment from other nurses is not always 'sisterly'. Enrolled nurses are particularly resentful that their contribution is all too often denied, or that they are not allowed any responsibility. This usually emerges as an attack on specific supervisors who are thought insensitive, or just plain 'snooty'. As one enrolled nurse complained, although she had been doing the job for six years, she was treated 'as though solid between the ears'. This encouraged an aggressive claim that enrolled nurses are 'the only ones doing the real nursing any more'. Their resentment is exacerbated because initiatives to undertake further training are discouraged or directly thwarted by senior registered staff. With their role and contribution devalued in this way, they vent their grievances against those immediately culpable, rather than the organisation of nursing itself. Some registered staff feel slighted by their colleagues, but these are invariably part-time staff who do not consider that they have been totally involved or accepted by full-timers. A relief sister summarised the views of several in her position: 'The permanent staff resents you, and you can't choose your off-duty hours, you just do what the permanent staff don't want.'

This friction between grades of nurse is compounded by the delegation of certain tasks to specific grades. This leads to considerable criticism that nursing is too routine, the pace of work has become too quick, the tasks are too fragmented, or the delegation of responsibility is all wrong. Nurses sense that new ideas are not welcomed. The ward routine is fixed, and overly bureaucratic. A sister sought another post where 'I can use more initiative and use my knowledge more fully.' The blame for the difficulties is invariably laid at the door of the nursing administration. And for those with several years' experience in the

profession, the decline is linked to the Salmon reforms. But whatever
the cause, young and old alike are greatly antagonistic to the excess of
red tape, supervisors and paperwork in which they feel engulfed. An
expression which occurred time and time again in our interviews
summed up this view: 'Too many chiefs and not enough Indians.'

Enrolled staff again decried what they saw as the particular
anomalies of their situation. We have already referred to the low level
of assignment in job tasks, and the lack of responsibility of which they
complain. The work delegated to them does not always have a clear
beneficial purpose, and this is made worse by its often tedious and
predictable character. The challenge that they expect is absent. Yet
other enrolled nurses find themselves with much day-to-day
responsibility because of staff shortages, but with scant official
recognition of their position. Thus the extent of job autonomy and
variety fluctuates — beyond their control. An older nurse confided that
it was particularly galling to be 'in charge' of the ward at one moment,
and then taking orders a little later 'from any student nurse who
happened to be around'. Irrespective of their contribution, they
complained that they were not included in important work discussions.
As if to prove that one cannot please everyone, however, there is a
contingent within the enrolled ranks who reject any extra duties, and
several in this grade justified their departure because of an inability, or
unwillingness, to 'cope with the responsibility'.

Staff nurses also complain of interference from above — especially
a 'meddling administration'. The latter is said to enjoy the best of both
worlds — at the expense of staff nurses. The administration can insist
that junior staff 'act-up' in an emergency, but do not accept with equal
alacrity that as administrators they should 'act-down' when the need
arises. The argument is that 'It's the administration that's given the
priority now — not the patients.' If the administration was not accused
of interfering, then it created a log-jam in decision-making because
no one appeared to know who had overall responsibility. In comparison
with their vitriolic comments about meddling from above, staff nurses
are much less critical of the rest of the nursing service.

The more senior registered grades are less inhibited in locating
inequities. They too attack the traditional scapegoat of all ward staff —
the nursing administrator. A top-heavy bureaucracy is charged with
looking for things to do 'to justify its existence'. As a result, much of
the autonomy that ward sisters anticipate has been usurped, and as one
charge nurse argued, 'the job is made far less challenging.' Quite simply,
while the pace of nursing has increased, so has the scope of the

administration, and the expanding tentacles of the beast have not only complicated, but also slowed down, the organisation of nursing. Many ward sisters are most unhappy about their transformation into mini-administrators with their consequent removal from the core activities of nursing. Hence the plaintive plea that they are too often not doing what they were trained for.

This can be expressed as a failure to identify an end product to their endeavours. In some areas, such as the extremes of intensive care and out-patients, nurses are unable to establish any real contact, or to see clear progress among the patients. This is where nursing comes close to a conveyor belt production line — where the 'throughput' of patients is rapid. It is not merely that nurses complain of being treated as 'numbers rather than people', but that they cannot avoid doing exactly the same to the patients. It is complemented by a lack of peer group involvement. This is the source of much resentment. There are plenty of opportunities for meeting people, but those with whom contact is made do not constitute 'friends'. Occasionally unpleasantness between staff creates acute discomfort, as wards fall victim to back-biting and malicious gossip as much as any virus. Nursing is then the loser.

The synthesis of these advantages and disadvantages in nursing depends on an estimate not only on their form, but their volume and intensity. There is little indication that nurses adopt a deep-rooted calculative orientation to their work. Instead the commitment ranges across relational and other intrinsic aspects. The espousal of job content is a function of the professional's mind as well as the predominance of females. Male nurses refer more regularly to nursing as a means to satisfy contextual needs and their positive views of job security in nursing, coupled with the prospects for promotion, are typical. They are also disinclined to mention the 'warm glow' of nursing sick people. Both sexes and all grades, however, emphasise the satisfaction derived when the work allows scope for judgement, challenge, discretion, responsibility and recognition. Explicit comparisons with other occupations are not made, although contrasts are drawn between nurses in other grades or wards.

Dissatisfaction in work at the level of rewards and working conditions provokes the most intense reaction. Disenchantment with job content is not dismissed lightly, but it does not create such basic indignation. The latter enjoys a latitude of toleration not accorded to the former. And yet contentment with pay and working conditions does not necessarily lead to, nor is it always associated with, intrinsic gratification. The picture is complicated since the work orientation of nurses is effectively mediated by domestic demands. The married woman, who works as much to get out of the house as because of her attachment to nursing, may gave a higher threshold of acceptance of poor conditions, since her employment alternatives are so limited. Another interpretation is that the higher-level advantages in work act as substitutes for each other, whereas disadvantages are cumulative. One really fulfilling aspect then exerts a disproportionate impact.

The behavioural reaction associated with these attitudinal stances is also far from straightforward. We reject immediately an explanation of turnover in terms of the simple equation: job satisfaction = low turnover; job dissatisfaction = high turnover. The previous statistical analysis and the present discussion of work orientation indicate a more circumscribed and complex relationship. Satisfaction, *per se*, is no guarantee that individuals will stay in their current post, when, for example, career goals take them elsewhere in the NHS, or domestic factors force them to take a break. Equally dissatisfaction may be associated with dropping out of nursing altogether, or moving to another hospital, or taking a break. Even here mobility is not inevitable, since other constraints may necessitate staying, such as the need for money or the lack of suitable, alternative employment.

Nurses' Own Perception of Mobility

The reasons offered by the leavers themselves for their departure from the current post confirms that their action has no straightforward connection with job satisfaction (see Table 5.1). Several of the most mentioned responses do not entail quitting the NHS. This applies with those undertaking a course of further training, as well as those moving to another hospital.

The other main category of leavers offer reasons associated with their domestic and family life. Pregnancy, marriage and spouse moving, together with looking after relatives, all rank prominently. Few of these explanations convey overt disaffection with the NHS, nursing or even particular institutions. The remainder imply a definite criticism of some part of the nursing service, although some are ambiguous. We include in the last category 'wanted a change'. This phrase encapsulates the high expectation of mobility which many nurses, especially among the newly qualified, hold. Some are glad to leave their present hospital, but for most the decision to try new pastures is justified less critically as, 'If I don't move now, I never will,' or 'I trained here, and I want to see other places.' A corresponding haziness is attached to the statement that nurses are returning home, to their own country, or going abroad.

Manifest criticism is generally phrased as an attack on the current hospital rather than on the NHS, although the distinction is not always clearly drawn. The most regular grouses relate to the impossible conditions under which nurses feel that they are expected to work, or are complaints about workmates or supervisors. Much is made of the hindrances to the provision of a proper nursing service, as if to affirm the professional commitment of those on the move.

A comparison of the reasons for leaving between the three grades further corroborates the lack of any simple association between job satisfaction and labour turnover. We have reported previously on the high separation rate among staff nurses, and the figures in Table 5.1 demonstrate that some reasons are characteristically staff-nurse dominated. The obvious concentration is in the further training and promotion categories. These are especially facilitated by the structure of nursing. The pattern is reinforced by the disproportionate location of young, single persons in this grade.

'Why are you staying?' can be an equally valid question. A high level of satisfaction is one associate of stability, but there are many other factors worthy of consideration. For example, even though individual nurses could get the promotion they want by moving elsewhere, they are tied to their present place of residence by family, or other social influences. Again, if the nurses' priorities are balanced in favour of non-work factors, a potential stimulus for mobility is nullified. The costs of movement in an economic and non-economic sense should not be underestimated. For most nurses it will involve leaving behind friends and a familiar locality and way of life. If there is a family and children to be considered, the pressures to stay put are even more difficult to ignore. Other costs apply to those who may contemplate leaving nursing altogether. All nursing staff have invested some years in obtaining their qualification, and they accumulate an emotional and economic attachment. They will regard themselves as nurses even when they have taken a break to look after their family. While this professional bond acts as a powerful counterweight to quitting, it may none the less stimulate movement between hospitals.

The attachment of nurses to their profession arises again in their statements about the most important aspect of their life. The central interests of most of those interviewed focus on home life, followed at a distance by work. In this predominantly female group, the discussion repeatedly veers towards husband, children and family matters. 'Husband first. Family second. Work third,' as a midwife summed up the majority opinion. To have a good marriage and relationship with

their spouse shines through in the replies. 'To create a good marriage.
My husband is more important than me. I have to take second place to
his work. I don't mind.' If still single, nurses show a determination to
'getting married', and to complete the impression that feminist attitudes
have made little headway: 'Looking forward to my marriage and
retirement from work.' For those with the first part of the family unit
behind them, the next step of starting a family or adding to the present
flock is the central discussion piece. 'The baby; I was set on a career,
but not now.' The most important motivation is then to establish a
happy home life. It is mentioned almost twice as often as work and
nursing. Among those who highlight their work as most central in
their life, the prevailing explanation is that nursing provides a valuable
and a valued service. 'Looking after patients, getting them better, seeing
them walk out again. You feel that you have achieved something.'
Nursing is especially seen in 'caring' terms, and in this sense it is
regularly described as 'fulfilling'. When phrased this way the orientation
follows traditional lines. The emphasis is on seeing people get better,
and looking after helpless people. It is far less often that the response
is couched in terms of the pursuit of professional knowledge, and its
application, 'Seeing that the patient gets correct treatment quickly and
efficiently.' In addition some senior staff refer to their enjoyment at
passing on their knowledge to learners, and there is an occasional
mention of the opportunities that further training allows to improve
nursing treatment of diseases and sick people.

If the preoccupation is not the family unit or nursing, it lies in
other non-work pursuits in one's free time. The accent is on central
life interests in leisure-time activities — especially holidays. It is more
often that young, single nurses make remarks such as 'Off-duty is
more important than on-duty time.' 'Saving money for a new car' and
similar instrumental attitudes are thin on the ground, but are not any
more noticeable among males. Interestingly, the latter express equal
concern with family matters, and do not provide a more heavily work-
oriented outlook than their female colleagues. Yet if male nurses are as
concerned to demonstrate their pre-eminent attachment to their family,
one doubts whether this emotional commitment demands the same
behavioural pattern from them as it does of female workers. The
contrast is vividly illustrated in further comments by those interviewed
on their likely condition in five years' time.

Again the replies are easily classified into a family and domestic
category, and another that refers to work-related matters. However,
many nurses spell out their views to encompass both. There is frequent

Table 5.1: Leavers' Own Perception of Mobility; by Grade of Nurse

Reasons	SEN	Staff Nurse	Ward Sister/ Charge Nurse	All (per cent)
Social/domestic				
Marriage	7	2	8	5
Pregnancy	10	14	20	14
Spouse moving	2	2	5	3
Other family reasons	6	5	8	6
Work-related				
Retirement	10	1	6	4
Further training	4	21	10	14
Promotion, better job	4	16	8	12
Want a change/going home	14	17	16	16
Dislike hospital/hours, etc./ quitting	17	10	5	10
Miscellaneous	7	3	2	4
No answer	19	9	9	13
N = 503	26	46	28	100

mention of starting a family, or increasing it. A discussion also gets
going of the intention to move their current place of residence. But
even when one foot is firmly planted at home, most are ambitious to
retain a link with nursing. The majority of imminent leavers, as well as
those remaining, affirm that they will still be nursing, albeit part-time.
The majority's future is of a dual life — at home, with husband and
children, and at work, part-time in the Health Service. Few nurses aim
to progress up the nursing hierarchy. The exceptions to this rule are the
male nurses. The charge nurse who proclaimed that he foresaw in five
years' time 'getting to the top. . .as a Divisional Nursing Officer if all
goes well' was more specific than most males, but in comparison, no
female nurse envisaged a career stretching through the upper levels of
the profession. The females are interested in horizontal mobility to
district nursing positions, and in further training to become Nurse
Tutors but little else.

Part of the explanation for this rests in their anticipated combination
of raising/looking after a family and working, but even those who
perceive a full-time career do not articulate a goal of promotion 'to the
top'.

Five years hence, nurses will still be nurses — in hospital or 'resting' at home, apart from a handful of enrolled staff who intend to exercise their nursing skills in allied areas — such as old people's homes, or doctors' surgeries. the motivation to maintain contact with work itself, and nursing in particular, is not dimmed. The ambition is rarely phrased in calculative terms. Work is propagandised for its intrinsic worth, its personal relationships, and for the contrast that it offers to the domestic routine. If nurses do not have the best of both worlds, this is as close as most envisage is practicable.

Summary

We started with a general finding from studies of professional workers that, unlike their manual counterparts, they treat work as their 'central life interest'. This professional ethos is cemented in the years of training, so that recruits are encouraged to regard the work setting as the main source of personal growth and social relationships. This contrasts with the alleged instrumental orientation of manual workers. Orzack's American study concluded that 'Professional nurses weight work settings more heavily than they weight non-work settings, with one exception: informal relations are somewhat more closely linked with non-work and community locations than is the case for general personal satisfaction.'[25] Our own research does not uncover the same overwhelming support for work as the central life interest of trained nurses. In our sample, work and family life rank more evenly, although many do not expect work relations to reach the same intensity as outside interests. Most importantly, nurses hope to complement their non-work life with their work interests, and vice versa. Orzack argues that 'the profession does not have appeals sufficient to outweigh role obligations required by non-professional groups in which its members participate.'[26] The domestic demands on female nurses are certainly keenly felt, but to leave work temporarily is not to downgrade their profession. Conversely, if males display more continuity in work, they are hardly less inclined to specify the significance of the non-work world.

It is in this context that the character and intensity of the work orientation mediates the potential for labour mobility experienced by trained nurses. There are within nursing employment in the NHS several structural constraints on labour mobility, such as the grade structure and the monopoly of jobs in the public sector. Against this it is relatively easy to transfer between nursing posts and some such movement is encouraged officially. This means that the occupational climate in nursing is far from antagonistic to labour mobility *per se*. It is justifiable in impeccable professional terms. Those who move between hospitals may therefore be demonstrating their acceptance of nursing practice, and of their commitment to nursing. A strong, or central, life interest in nursing may actually stimulate labour mobility. Staff need not be satisfied with their current institution, but they are sufficiently contented to stay within nursing. (Of course, there is also a small minority whose continued presence in nursing is less positive.) Even among the leavers who are giving up work altogether there is a sizeable proportion who are contemplating a speedy return to the service. As described, many are leaving the NHS because of domestic circumstances over which they have little control. Thus to claim that if a nurse leaves, for example because of pregnancy, then she is demonstrating that her central life interest is not in her work is both hollow and misleading. The women in our sample do not automatically set work pleasures against those of the outside life, although often they are obliged to choose in practice. Indeed one might easily interpret the high intention to return to nursing as, if anything, a sign that work is accorded at least equal priority. Although an indication of nurses' orientation to work and their level of satisfaction with those expectations are important criteria of the likelihood of labour turnover, they only constitute a partial explanation. Instead we view nursing turnover as a complex interaction of: domestic and personal circumstances; work features and constraints; plus the orientation to work, which incorporates both the character and level of job expectation and satisfaction.

Notes

1. For an 'academic' debate of the main issues, see J.H. Goldthorpe, 'Attitudes and Behaviour of Car Assembly Workers: a Deviant Case and a Theoretical Critique', *British Journal of Sociology*, vol.17 (1966), pp.227-44; W. Daniel, 'Industrial Behaviour and Orientation to Work – a Critique', *Journal of Management Studies*, vol.6 (1969), pp.366-75; J.H. Goldthorpe, 'The Social Action Approach to Industrial Sociology – a Reply to Daniel', *Journal of Management Studies*, vol.7 (1970), pp.199-208; W. Daniel, 'Productivity Bargaining and Orientation to Work – a Rejoinder to Goldthorpe'. *Journal of Management Studies*, vol.8 (1971), pp.329-35; J.H. Goldthorpe. 'Daniel on Orientation to Work – a Final Comment', *Journal of Management Studies*. vol.9 (1972), pp.266-73; F. Herzberg, B. Mausner and B. Synderman, *The Motivation to Work* (Wiley, New York, 1959); V. Vroom, *Work and Motivation* (Wiley New York, 1964).

2. Daniel, 'Industrial Behaviour and Orientation to Work', p.367.

3. Ibid., p.367.

4. K. Hawkins, *Conflict and Change* (Holt, Rinehart and Winston, New York, 1972), pp.30-1.

5. R. Bendix, *Work and Authority in Industry* (Harper and Row, New York. 1963), p.312.

6. Hawkins, *Conflict and Change*, p.33.

7. A.H. Maslow, *Motivation and Personality* (Harper and Row. New York, 1954); Herzberg *et al.*, *The Motivation to Work*.

8. R. Blauner, *Alienation and Freedom* (University of Chicago Press, Chicago 1964), p.37.

9. Ibid., p.15. The notion of alienation has provoked a considerable literature. For example, I. Meszaros, *Marx's Theory of Alienation* (Merlin, London, 1970); and for a graphic picture of life in a contemporary car factory: H. Beynon, *Working for Ford* (Allen Lane, London, 1973).

10. Blauner, *Alienation and Freedom*, pp.24-6.

11. J.H. Goldthorpe, D. Lockwood, F. Bechhofer and J. Platt, *The Affluent Worker: Industrial Attitudes and Behaviour* (Cambridge |University Press, Cambridge 1968); D. Wedderburn and R. Crompton, *Workers' Attitudes and Technology* (Cambridge University Press, Cambridge, 1972).

12. Goldthorpe, 'The Social Action Approach to Industrial Sociology', p.207.

13. R. Hyman, 'Economic Motivation and Labour Stability', *British Journal of Industrial Relations*, vol.8 (1970), pp.159-78; S. Saleh and J. Hyde, 'Intrinsic vs. Extrinsic Orientation and Job Satisfaction', *Occupational Psychology*, vol.43 (1969), pp.47-53; C. Alderfer, 'An Empirical Test of a Theory of Human|Needs, *Organisational Behaviour and Human Performance*, vol.4 (1969), pp.142-75.

14. R. Dubin, 'Industrial Workers' Worlds: a Study of the "Central Life Interests" of Industrial Workers', *Social Problems*, vol.3 (1956), pp.131-42; L. Orzack, 'Work as a "Central Life Interest" of Professionals', *Social Problems*, vol.7 (1959), pp.125-32.

15. The phrases are applied negatively in the Affluent Worker Study: Goldthorpe *et al.*, *The Affluent Worker: Industrial Attitudes and Behaviour*, p.39.

16. Orzack, 'Work as a "Central Life Interest" of Professionals'; Morton-Williams and Berthoud, 'Nurse Interview Survey'; MacGuire, *Threshold to Nursing*, pp.35-49.

17. R. Habenstein and E. Christ, *Professionaliser, Traditionaliser and Utiliser* (University of Missouri, Columbia, 1955).

18. F. Matz, 'Nurses' in A. Etzioni (ed.), *The Semi-Professions and Their Organisation* (Free Press, Glencoe, 1969), p.68.

19. MacGuire, *Threshold to Nursing*, pp.35-49.

20. All quotations henceforward in this chapter which have no footnote are taken verbatim from interviews with leavers or stayers in our own study.

21. Morton-Williams and Berthoud, 'Nurse Interview Survey', pp.4-6.

22. M. Weir (ed.), *Job Satisfaction* (Fontana, Glasgow, 1976).

23. A comparable study among nursing administrators is C. White and M.C. MacGuire, 'Job Satisfaction and Dissatisfaction amongst Hospital Nursing Supervisors', *Nursing Research*, vol.22, no.1 (1973), pp.25-30.

24. *Report of the Committee on Nursing Pay* (Halsbury Report) (DHSS, London, 1974).

25. Orzack, 'Work as a "Central Life Interest" of Professionals', p.57.

26. Ibid., p.57.

6 REFLECTIONS ON NURSING TURNOVER

This book has explored several aspects of labour turnover in nursing. The stimulus was the concern expressed within the National Health Service about its difficulties in retaining its trained nursing staff. Our objective has been to specify the level and variation in turnover, together with the conditions under which such behaviour takes place. We have extended the traditional purview of turnover investigations beyond the immediate workplace to incorporate a range of outside social and personal factors. The presumption has been that an explanation of labour turnover must consider the wider orientation to work within the structural constraints of the time. The decision to stay, or leave, is the function of an often complex social process and demands a similarly flexible approach by those intent on treatment and/or explanation.

The nurses that came under our gaze were predominantly young, recently qualified, and not long in their current post. The mean length of service in the latter was fractionally over three years, and while 75 per cent of nurses had stayed for less than five years, at least 25 per cent had been in post less than one year. A slightly less short-stay picture, however, is gained from the length of service figures for time served in the current hospital, since a notable minority of nurses have either obtained promotion without changing institutions, or have returned to their former employer after an interlude elsewhere. Nevertheless the majority of trained staff currently in work qualified within the last ten years.

In aggregate terms, the crude separation rate indicates that one in four nurses leave their current place of employment each year. The loss of members from cohorts of new entrants to individual hospitals during the first year's service is approximately one in three. The higher mobility demonstrated by the cohort figures compared with the crude separation rate highlights the strong propensity to leave among recent recruits. The association between turnover and length of service thereafter fluctuates — with the effect of grade most evident. Newly qualified nurses are especially liable to quit relatively soon after appointment in apparent eagerness to avail themselves of the earliest opportunities to live and work in a fresh environment. After this initial outflow, departures wane until the shuffling feet are heard again after about a year in post. The 'roller-coaster' pattern of later years applies to most groups, although the peaks and troughs occur at different time intervals.

This picture bears a surface correspondence to the 'Tavistock Model'. However, closer inspection raises several question marks against the 'induction crisis-differential transit-settled connection' continuum. The initial losses are not concentrated in the first one or two months after appointment, but after six to eight months. Equally noteworthy, the force of separation coefficients undermine arguments about a growing assimilation of employees into the organisation. If leaving does become less probable over time, the trend is far from clear-cut, and not evident at all in some groups of nurses. It is the rise and fall in transition propensities which is more striking than claims of a movement towards a settled connection.

One clue to the more irregular pattern of turnover among nurses lies in the direction of mobility upon departure. This divides between leaving work altogether and transferring to another hospital. The absence of movement to non-NHS nursing, or to another occupation, implies that an attachment to the profession has been established which supersedes any link to a particular institution. Further confirmation that turnover is far from reducible to an individual's ability to assimilate into specific organisations, or to an organisation's success at integrating its employees, lies in the leavers' own perception of mobility. Much of the loss to a specific hospital does not reflect on its efficiency as an employer. In some cases hospitals|encourage movement within the service as a means of extending individuals' experience, and in other instances they are impotent to affect the decision to leave because they cannot offer the further training or the promotion which the nurse wants. In addition, a hospital is often in a weak bargaining position to retain its staff when such a significant proportion quits because of outside considerations — especially domestic, family matters. References to an induction crisis as the sole explanation of early leaving are similarly wide of the mark. Trained nurses have already spent several years in hospitals as learners, and even when they take a first post after qualification in another hospital, the conditions which have sparked off their move are not typically associated with the novelty of their new position. Conversely, not all of the staying results from the progressive realisation that one has a place in the organisation, but instead stems from the difficulties of moving elsewhere.

Our doubts about the efficacy of the Tavistock model, and its apparent organisational determinism, are reinforced by detailed examination of the conditions under which turnover occurs. The nurses' own forecast of their behaviour is in an unchallenged position as the pre-eminent guide to stability or movement. This brings out the element of calculation and planning that underlies labour turnover. Apart from this factor, the spotlight falls most brightly on those features which relate to the constraints and possibilities of movement — both in and out of work. For example, grade, size of hospital where working and length of service in current post all demonstrate some predictive effect. Work attitudes are rather less successful, and the relationship is not always in the direction anticipated. It remains for personal and domestic conditions to substantiate the impact of non-work factors. Age, sex, marital status and whether the nurse (if female) has any young children all gain prominence. To stay or to leave, particularly after a short period in post, is a decision taken by (and in some instances almost taken for) nurses against this complex backcloth. It encompasses the desire to get on, to see new places, to have children, and the ease with which these and other expectations may be achieved. In consequence, the prediction of turnover *per se* in a heterogeneous population, as are trained nursing staff, has little chance of pronounced success.

This is highlighted in the association between work attitudes and nursing turnover. A typical conclusion of previous research on other occupational groups has been that satisfaction exerts a direct effect on labour mobility. And yet in practice, while dissatisfied nurses do quit their post, the satisfied are as likely to move, or give up work, temporarily perhaps, as stay. The motivation and ability to work is a function of more than what goes on in the immediate work-place. This is most prominent in a predominantly female work-force, where outside role obligations create strong pressures. It is not that women are less committed to nursing than their male colleagues. The expectations of the latter, however, are geared more exclusively to work, whereas women must attend to both work and home. To comprehend nursing turnover requires a thorough examination of individuals' priorities across their work and non-work lives, and what conditions structure their views. The location of the meeting point between the desirability and the ease of movement cannot therefore be drawn in with great precision, unless the group under inspection are much more homogeneous than the trained nurse category. It is an unfortunate corollary of this complexity that research has got bogged down in a crude empiricism where the statistical effect of turnover's correlates has been elevated above their explanatory virtue.

This extension of the range of labour turnover research goes hand in hand with a review of several other prevalent misconceptions and confusion about the nature of this phenomenon. Manpower planning in the NHS is still in its infancy, and in nursing the shortages of information and expertise to which Briggs referred are being attended to with not a little professional scepticism. Yet the reaction of nurse managers cannot all be put down to gross complacency. Is it the case that labour turnover among trained nurses is running at a wholly unacceptable level? The presumption that a particular rate is 'high' or 'low' begs the question: high in relation to what? A comparison of the mobility of nurses and social workers or primary school teachers is not a wholly satisfactory response. For it is not determined what level of turnover can reasonably be contained by the relevant organisation before its clients suffer. Yet it is one of the enduring assumptions about labour turnover that it is harmful to the functioning of any organisation. If departures and recruitment are at such a level that new staff are coming on to the ward each week, one is inclined to accept this pessimistic view, but in other circumstances the benefits of labour turnover should not be forgotten. Labour movement can promote efficiency and work relations. The heart of the problem is to ensure a balance between the need to establish some continuity in patient care, and the desire to provide nursing staff with a varied and challenging environment.

The costs of turnover more directly stem from the financial burden of hiring and training replacements for those staff who have left, which is over and above any inefficiency which ensues while the recruits are familiarised to their new surroundings. This argument is reinforced in nursing by the considerable number of trained staff not currently employed in the service. And yet the costs of inducting a qualified nurse into a new hospital are often exaggerated. Most significantly, a relatively common set of standards and techniques of nursing practice applies across hospitals so that the transfer of individual skills from one institution to another is a comparatively painless task. The paradox is that that feature which encourages retention in nursing because of interchangeable skills also stimulates movement within the service.

This also raises doubts about the success with which nursing administrators in individual hospitals can intervene to dampen the level, or to change the character, of nursing mobility. The confidence of many in authority that such mobility can be checked is seriously misplaced and even the most ingenious manager would be driven to distraction in order to come up with a solution. Most departees were intent on leaving for domestic and personal reasons, or else wanted to

live and work in another place simply for a change of scenery. Some
would have remained, but only if promoted, or given the exact course
of further training that they required. These matters are not equally
amenable to simple ameliorative action. Our impression is that in the
formulation of policies to alleviate nursing turnover, too little
recognition is paid to the difficulties of being a woman in work with
domestic obligations. While there is little room for administrative
intervention in the role(s) played by women there is scope for the
Health Service to aid individuals' ability to cope with both job and
family by, for example, the provision of more nursery facilities.

There is also a suspicion that the interpretation of labour turnover
(or the more revealing insistence within the Health Service on 'wastage')
has cast the phenomenon in terms of departures *per se.* As we have
described the process, nursing mobility encompasses two main types:
one, which leads out of work altogether, and a second, which takes the
nurse to another hospital. While the latter constitutes a loss to
individual institutions, the service as a whole may benefit from this
exchange of staff. As a group, nurses remain attached to their chosen
profession and the opportunities which it provides them. Even among
those who quit the service there is a determination to re-establish a link
with nursing in the future. It is this aspect of labour turnover which has
been so much neglected — namely, the return of people into paid
employment after a break. There is a large reserve pool of currently
unemployed trained nurses, many of whom anticipate their return to
the NHS. Efforts to bring about a reduction in departures might
therefore reap commensurate profit by facilitating the return and
recruitment of already qualified nurses. The growth of 'nurse-banks',
more in-service and refresher courses and the establishment of an
up-to-date register of trained staff all offer scope for management
action.

Within the hospital there are several sources of acute and perhaps
growing disenchantment, which may be harbingers of worsening
difficulties with labour turnover in the future. Part of these relate to
the opportunities for self-advancement, but most revolve around the
system of rewards which are provided — both in terms of pay and
prospects, as well as of status within the nursing establishment.
Remedial action by management which concentrates upon some aspect
of 'job enrichment' can only go so far; and more fundamental changes
await national decisions. We have mentioned at several points the
noticeable disenchantment with their position expressed by enrolled
nurses. No significant effect on their perceived disadvantages as a grade

can be expected of local initiatives. This also illustrates the indeterminancy of district action in labour turnover and manpower planning generally. The NHS 'firm' is a national employer and individual nurses are able to plug into this wider network of opportunities over the heads of their local employers. When one adds to this picture the wider social and economic forces that alternatively stimulate and depress labour mobility more generally, the lot of the nurse manpower planner is far from a happy one.

To conclude, nursing turnover cannot be isolated from the mixture of work and non-work conditions in which it is located. It is a social process and a full explanation must take proper account of this fact. If the career of a nurse does not span a lifetime in nursing, we shall rarely understand why if the study is restricted to the world of nursing alone.

APPENDIX: FIRST-WAVE QUESTIONNAIRE

First of all, we should like to ask you some questions about your work in nursing.

Office use

1. What is the name and location of the hospital where you did your first training as a nurse/midwife?

.... — 111-12

2. In what year did you *first* qualify as a nurse/midwife? .... — 113-14

3. Did you have any other full-time job *prior* to training as a nurse?

Yes	( )		1 115
No	( ) Go to Q.4		5

3a. What sort of job was it? Be as exact as possible.

.... — 116-17

4. What sort of jobs have you had as a nurse, in or outside the NHS? Describe present post, and up to *5* previous posts, if you have had that many. (*Please note*: a change in post means here either a change in employer/hospital, *or* a change of grade in the same hospital.)

	Name of Hospital or Employer	Grade or Position held	Dates of service	
Present post				— 118-19 20, 21, 22
Previous post(s) 1.				— 123-24 25, 26, 27
2.				— 128-29 30, 31, 32
3.				— 133-34 35, 36, 37
4.				— 138-39 40, 41, 42
5.				— 143-44 45, 46, 47
				n: j148 n:h149

5. How many years have you been at this hospital? Include time spent as a student/pupil nurse if applicable. ...... — 150-51

6. Do you work full or part-time in your present post?

		Office Use
Full-time ( ) Go to Q.7	1	152
Part-time: hours per week		
Under 10 ( )	2	
10-19 ( )	3	
20-29 ( )	4	
30 plus ( )	5	

6a. Do you feel that part-time nurses are accepted by the full-time nursing staff in this hospital?

Yes ( ) Go to Q. 7	1	153
No ( )	5	

6b. Why do you say that? .... — 154

.... — 155

7. On what *type of ward* do you work? .... — 156

8. On what shift do you work at present?

Earlies ( )	1	157
Lates ( )	2	
Splits ( )	3	
Nights ( )	4	
Other (specify)	5	

9. Have you been in continuous employment, in the NHS, since qualifying, or have you had any breaks, that is, spent more than 6 months at a time away from nursing?

I have never been out of the NHS ( ) Go to Q.10	5	158
I've had one break only ( )	1	
I've had two breaks ( )	2	
I've had three or more breaks ( )	3	

9a. What were the reasons for having your break(s)?

		Yes	No	1:5
i.	Getting married	( )	( )	159
ii.	Starting a family	( )	( )	160
iii.	Husband/wife moving	( )	( )	161
iv.	Wanted a rest from work	( )	( )	162
v.	Disliked nursing work	( )	( )	163
vi.	Disliked nursing pay	( )	( )	164
vii.	Wanted to get out of nursing	( )	( )	165
viii.	Preferred nursing outside the NHS	( )	( )	166

9b. What sort of job did you do?
(Be as exact as possible, including whether it was full or part-time.)

.... — 167

9c. Why did you return to NHS nursing?   Office Use

		Yes	No	1:5
i.	Able to leave family	( )	( )	168
ii.	Family/own health improved	( )	( )	169
iii.	Wanted to get out of house	( )	( )	170
iv.	Needed the money	( )	( )	171
v.	Preferred NHS nursing pay	( )	( )	172
vi.	Preferred NHS nursing working conditions	( )	( )	173
vii.	Other (specify)			174

10. Do you think it is likely that you will be leaving this hospital within the next year or not?

Definitely will *not* leave	( ) Go to Q.11	4	175
The situation is uncertain	( )	3	
Slight chance I will leave	( )	2	
Definitely will leave	( )	1	

10a. Why might you leave? .... — 176

.... — 177

....

11. Now for some questions about your work. How do you see your job as a nurse?

Here is a list of 10 pairs of words and phrases people use to describe their work, and in between each pair is a measuring stick of seven boxes, (_). Taking the first pair of words — Dull/Exciting — as an example, the box on the extreme left would mean that the job is *very dull*, for you, the next box would mean that it was *fairly dull*, and so on. The words at the top of the columns will help you to choose the box you think most appropriate.

Now please mark with a tick (√), how you see your work as a nurse.

	Very	Fairly	Slightly	Neither	Slightly	Fairly	Very		1-7
ull	(_)	(_)	(_)	(_)	(_)	(_)	(_)	Exciting	— 211
mplicated	(_)	(_)	(_)	(_)	(_)	(_)	(_)	Straightforward	— 212
uaranteed	(_)	(_)	(_)	(_)	(_)	(_)	(_)	Insecure	— 213
ken for anted	(_)	(_)	(_)	(_)	(_)	(_)	(_)	Respected	— 214
rsonal	(_)	(_)	(_)	(_)	(_)	(_)	(_)	Impersonal	— 215
d-fashioned	(_)	(_)	(_)	(_)	(_)	(_)	(_)	Modern	— 216
utine	(_)	(_)	(_)	(_)	(_)	(_)	(_)	Varied	— 217
ean	(_)	(_)	(_)	(_)	(_)	(_)	(_)	Dirty	— 218
st	(_)	(_)	(_)	(_)	(_)	(_)	(_)	Slow	— 219
egimented	(_)	(_)	(_)	(_)	(_)	(_)	(_)	Free of restrictions	— 220

12. In general, would you say that you are well informed, or not,   Office Use
about your work as a nurse, in this hospital?

Very well informed	( )	1 221
Well informed	( )	2
Badly informed	( )	4
Very badly informed	( )	5
Not sure	( )	3

13. Are you satisfied, or not, with the *information* you receive about
the following aspects of your work in this hospital?
(Give one tick for each aspect, except where one of these points
does not apply to your particular work, then leave that aspect
blank.)

	Very satisfied	Satisfied	Neither	Dissatisfied	Very dissatisfied	1:5
A. The ward procedure book	(_)	(_)	(_)	(_)	(_)	222
B. Priority of work tasks	(_)	(_)	(_)	(_)	(_)	223
C. Working with new machinery	(_)	(_)	(_)	(_)	(_)	224
D. New medical developments in your field	(_)	(_)	(_)	(_)	(_)	225
E. Future changes affecting your work routine	(_)	(_)	(_)	(_)	(_)	226
F. *Major* items of equipment	(_)	(_)	(_)	(_)	(_)	227
G. *Minor* items of equipment	(_)	(_)	(_)	(_)	(_)	228
H. Vacancies on other shifts/wards	(_)	(_)	(_)	(_)	(_)	229

14. In general, would you say that you are dissatisfied or satisfied
about the *overall organisation* of this hospital?

Very satisfied	( )	1 230
Satisfied	( )	2
Dissatisfied	( )	4
Very dissatisfied	( )	5
Not sure	( )	3

15. Do you feel well or badly *informed* about the following in this   Office Use
    hospital?

	Very well informed	Well informed	Neither	Badly informed	Very badly informed	1:5
A. The nursing grade structure	(_)	(_)	(_)	(_)	(_)	231
B. Hospital budget	(_)	(_)	(_)	(_)	(_)	232
C. Work of nursing administrators	(_)	(_)	(_)	(_)	(_)	233
D. Work of hospital doctors	(_)	(_)	(_)	(_)	(_)	234
E. Work of ancillary staff	(_)	(_)	(_)	(_)	(_)	235
F. Work of para-medical staff	(_)	(_)	(_)	(_)	(_)	236
G. Future expansion of hospital	(_)	(_)	(_)	(_)	(_)	237

16. Does your immediate supervisor allow you to do your work as
    you want to do it or not?

Yes, most of the time	( )	1	238
Yes, some of the time	( )	2	
No, not very often	( )	4	
No, not at all	( )	5	
Not sure	( )	3	

17. If you have any suggestion for improving your job, or changing
    the set-up in the ward in some way, how easy or difficult is it
    for you to *persuade* your immediate supervisor?

Very difficult	( )	5	239
Difficult	( )	4	
Easy	( )	2	
Very easy	( )	1	
Not sure	( )	3	

18. How much *influence* do you feel that you have on the following aspects of your work — a lot or not very much? (Give one tick for each aspect, except where one of these points does not apply to your particular work, then leave that aspect blank.)

Office Use

1:5

	A lot of	Some influence	Not sure	Little influence	No influence at all	
A. Which shift you work	(_)	(_)	(_)	(_)	(_)	240
B. Total hours worked	(_)	(_)	(_)	(_)	(_)	241
C. Which ward you work	(_)	(_)	(_)	(_)	(_)	242
D. Pace of work	(_)	(_)	(_)	(_)	(_)	243
E. Priority of work to be done	(_)	(_)	(_)	(_)	(_)	244
F. *Minor* items of equipment	(_)	(_)	(_)	(_)	(_)	245
G. *Major* items of equipment	(_)	(_)	(_)	(_)	(_)	246
H. Physical conditions, noise, heat, etc.	(_)	(_)	(_)	(_)	(_)	247
I. Arrangement of ward facilities, size of room, number of beds, etc.	(_)	(_)	(_)	(_)	(_)	248
J. Who you work with	(_)	(_)	(_)	(_)	(_)	249
K. Frequency, length of breaks	(_)	(_)	(_)	(_)	(_)	250
L. General quality of patient care	(_)	(_)	(_)	(_)	(_)	251

19. Does your hospital organise regular meetings for nurses of your grade to discuss problems and changes in your work?   Office Use

                Yes   ( )   1 252

                No   ( ) Go to Q.20 5

IF YES: 19a. Do you think these meetings are:

                Very worthwhile ( )   1 253

                Mixed feelings ( )   3

                Waste of time ( )   5

20. Listed below are a number of questions about work. How far on balance do you feel they apply to your work as a nurse/midwife?

		Yes	No	1:5
a)	First, do you have to work too fast, most of the time?	( )	( )	254
b)	Are you exhausted when you finish work?	( )	( )	255
c)	Does your work demand enough of you?	( )	( )	256
d)	Does your work give you a real chance to try out ideas of your own?	( )	( )	257
e)	Can you do your work, and think about other things most of the time?	( )	( )	258
f)	On a normal workday, do you have the opportunity to make your own decisions when you are carrying out your tasks?	( )	( )	259
g)	Can you see the end product of your work?	( )	( )	260
h)	Are you under constant supervision in your work?	( )	( )	261
i)	Are you doing a lot of work other than what you were trained for?	( )	( )	262

21. Do you have any close friends at this hospital, or not?

                One or two ( )   1 263

                Three to five ( )   2

                Half a dozen or more ( )   3

                I have no close friends here ( ) Go to Q.23 5

22. Do you see these close friends outside working hours?

                Almost every day ( )   1 264

                Several times a week ( )   2

                Several times a month ( )   3

                Hardly at all ( )   4

166 *Appendix*

23. What do you think, as a rule, of the trained nursing staff you work with? As in question 11, you will find below a list of 10 pairs of words you might use to describe your fellow employees. Taking the first pair of words — slow/fast — as an example, the box on the extreme left would mean that they were *very slow*, the next box would mean that they were *fairly slow*, and so on. The words at the top of the columns will help you to choose the box you think is appropriate.

Office Use

Now please mark in how you see the trained nurses you work with.

	Very	Fairly	Slightly	Neither	Slightly	Fairly	Very		
Slow	(_)	(_)	(_)	(_)	(_)	(_)	(_)	Fast	265
Imaginative	(_)	(_)	(_)	(_)	(_)	(_)	(_)	Dull	266
Withdrawn	(_)	(_)	(_)	(_)	(_)	(_)	(_)	Outgoing	267
Casual	(_)	(_)	(_)	(_)	(_)	(_)	(_)	Precise	268
Modern	(_)	(_)	(_)	(_)	(_)	(_)	(_)	Old-fashioned	269
Disciplinarians	(_)	(_)	(_)	(_)	(_)	(_)	(_)	Easy-going	270
Ambitious	(_)	(_)	(_)	(_)	(_)	(_)	(_)	Content with their lot	271
Progressive	(_)	(_)	(_)	(_)	(_)	(_)	(_)	Reactionary	272
Rigid	(_)	(_)	(_)	(_)	(_)	(_)	(_)	Flexible	273
Dependable	(_)	(_)	(_)	(_)	(_)	(_)	(_)	Unpredictable	274

24. There is a shortage of trained nurses in some parts of Britain. What improvements do you think are necessary to encourage *trained nurses to stay* in the NHS?

	Very important	Important	Neither	Not important	Very unimportant	1:5
A. Relaxation of discipline	(_)	(_)	(_)	(_)	(_)	311
B. Better promotion possibilities	(_)	(_)	(_)	(_)	(_)	312
C. Increased salary	(_)	(_)	(_)	(_)	(_)	313
D. Regular training opportunities	(_)	(_)	(_)	(_)	(_)	314
E. More auxiliary help	(_)	(_)	(_)	(_)	(_)	315
F. More flexible hours	(_)	(_)	(_)	(_)	(_)	316
G. Special responsibility pay	(_)	(_)	(_)	(_)	(_)	317

H. Shorter work working week	(_)	(_)	(_)	(_)	(_)	318
I. Allow nurses split time between hospital and community	(_)	(_)	(_)	(_)	(_)	319
J. More nursing accommodation	(_)	(_)	(_)	(_)	(_)	320
K. Creche/ nursery facilities	(_)	(_)	(_)	(_)	(_)	321

25. Compared to *the effort that you put into your job*, how do you feel about the pay you receive as a nurse? Is it good, bad or about right?

Office Use

Compared with the effort, my pay is:

Very bad	( )	1	322
Bad	( )	2	
About right	( )	3	
Good	( )	4	
Very good	( )	5	

26. Compared to the effort that *other nurses of your grade* make in this hospital, how do you feel about the pay you receive? Is it good, bad, or about right?

Compared to the effort of other nurses of my grade:

My pay is very good	( )	1	323
Good	( )	2	
About right	( )	3	
Bad	( )	4	
Very bad	( )	5	

27. How do you feel about the pay you receive compared to the *contribution you make to the running of this hospital*? Is it bad, good, or about right?

Compared to my contribution:

My pay is very good	( )	1	324
Good	( )	2	
About right	( )	3	
Bad	( )	4	
Very bad	( )	5	

28. *Compared to groups outside nursing*, would you say that nurses are well or badly paid?

Compared to others, nurses are:

Very badly paid	( )	1	325

Badly paid	( )	2
About right	( )	3
Well paid	( )	4
Very well paid	( )	5

29. What are *the promotion prospects* in nursing for someone like yourself, good or bad?

Very good	( )	1	326
Fairly good	( )	2	
Not too good	( )	4	
Very bad	( )	5	
About right	( )	3	

30. Would it be easy or not for you to find a nursing job, as good as the one you now have, in another hospital?

Office Use

Very easy	( )	1	327
Easy	( )	2	
Not sure	( )	3	
Difficult	( )	4	
Very difficult	( )	5	

31. Are there jobs *outside the NHS* where you would be able to use your nursing experience and be in a better position than your present one?

Yes	( )	1	328
No	( ) Go to Q. 32	5	

IF YES: 31a. What jobs are they?   329

. . . .   30, 31

. . . .   32

32. Which of the following occupations do you think is similar in status to nursing and which do you think is different?

	Higher status than nursing	Similar to nursing	Lower than nursing	1:3
a. Social worker	( )	( )	( )	333
b. Radiographer	( )	( )	( )	334
c. Air steward/ess	( )	( )	( )	335
d. Schoolteacher	( )	( )	( )	336
e. Actor/actress	( )	( )	( )	337

33. Do you read nursing journals such as *Nursing Times* and *Nursing Mirror* or not?

Yes, regularly	( )	1	338
Occasionally	( )	2	
Only when I'm looking for jobs	( )	3	
No, I don't read them	( )	5	

Office Use

34. How far do you agree or disagree with the following statements?

	Agree strongly	Agree	Not sure	Disagree	Disagree strongly	
A. It is only natural that women devote their lives to looking after home and family.	(_)	(_)	(_)	(_)	(_)	339
B. We are now entering a time when more wives will be the main providers.	(_)	(_)	(_)	(_)	(_)	340
C. There is something unattractive about women who are more concerned with a career than with a family and home.	(_)	(_)	(_)	(_)	(_)	341
D. Being at home all day is boring and frustrating.	(_)	(_)	(_)	(_)	(_)	342
E. Most married women only go out to work because of financial pressure.	(_)	(_)	(_)	(_)	(_)	343
F. Men are always given preference over women when it comes to promotion at work.	(_)	(_)	(_)	(_)	(_)	344
G. It is a waste that highly trained women devote their lives to looking after a home.	(_)	(_)	(_)	(_)	(_)	345
H. For men, work is a central life concern, while for women work is no more than a stop-gap measure.	(_)	(_)	(_)	(_)	(_)	346

35. Are you a member of any of the following organisations?

		Yes	No	1:5
a)	COHSE	( )	( )	347
b)	NALGO	( )	( )	348
c)	NUPE	( )	( )	349
d)	Royal College of Midwives	( )	( )	350
e)	Royal College of Nursing	( )	( )	351
f)	Other (specify)			352

36. Do you hold an official position, such as officer, committee member, in any of the above organisations?

Yes	( )	1 353
No	( )	5
Not a member	( )	0

37. Do you attend meetings of your association or union regularly or not?

Yes, most meetings	( )	1 354
Fairly often	( )	2
Occasionally	( )	3
Hardly at all	( )	4
Never	( )	5
Not a member	( )	0

38. Do you attend meetings (conferences, institutes, workshops, etc.) inside and/or outside the hospital, devoted to matters relevant to nursing?

Yes, inside hospital only	( )	1 355
Yes, outside hospital only	( )	2
Yes, inside *and* outside hospital	( )	3
No	( )	5

Now, we should like to end by asking some questions about yourself.

39. Firstly, what sex are you?

Female	( )	1 356
Male	( )	3

Office Use

40. What is your marital status?

Single	( ) Go to Q.41	1 357
Married	( )	2
Widowed	( )	3
Divorced/separated	( )	4

40a. Do you have any children?

Yes	( )	1 358
No	( ) Go to Q.40e	5

                                          Yes   No   1:5

40b. Do you have any children still at school? ( ) ( )   359

40c. Do you have any children of pre-school age?   ( ) ( )   360

40d. Have all your children left school? ( ) ( )   361

40e. What is/was the occupation of your husband/wife?
(Be as exact as possible and give skill/grade level. If housewife, unemployed, retired or student, please indicate.)   362, 63, 64

. . . .

41. How old are you?

20 to 24 years	( )	1 365
25 to 29 years	( )	2
30 to 34 years	( )	3
35 to 39 years	( )	4
40 to 44 years	( )	5
45 to 49 years	( )	6
50 to 54 years	( )	7
55 or above	( )	8

42. What nationality are you? 366

43. Where were your parents born?

	Father	Mother	
United Kingdom	( )	( )	1 367
Eire	( )	( )	2
Europe	( )	( )	3
New Commonwealth (e.g. India, Pakistan, West Indies)	( )	( )	4
Old Commonwealth (e.g. Australia, Canada, New Zealand)	( )	( )	5
Other (specify)		( )	6

Office Use

**44. What was your father's main occupation while you were
growing up?**

368,

. . . .   69, 70

45. Have you any of the following educational qualifications?

	Yes	No	1:5
a. CSE and/or O levels	( )	( )	411
b. A levels and/or Higher Grade	( )	( )	412
c. Degree	( )	( )	413
d. Other (specify)			414

None 415

46. How are you placed with respect to housing/accommodation?

Own/buying a house	( )	1 416
Living with relatives	( )	2
Renting (other than hospital accommodation)	( )	3
Renting hospital accommodation	( )	4
Other (specify)		5, 6

47. About how far do you live from the hospital?

Less than one mile	( )	1 417
1 to 4 miles	( )	2
5 to 9 miles	( )	3
10 or more miles	( )	4

**48. How do you feel about your neighbourhood as a place to live in?
That is, do you:**

Like it very much	( )	1 418
Like it somewhat	( )	2
Dislike it	( )	3
Dislike it very much	( )	4
Not sure	( )	5

**49. Do you belong to any non-nursing clubs or organisations?
(Such as Church group, political party, PTA).**

Yes	( )	1 419
No	( ) Go to Q. 50	5

IF YES: **49a. Do you hold an official position in any of these
clubs/associations?**

Yes	( )	1 420
No	( )	5

49b. About how often do you go to meetings of these organisations?

Office Use

At least once a week	( )	1 421
A few times a month	( )	2
A few times a year	( )	3
Hardly ever	( )	4
Never	( )	5

50. And finally, if you could go back to when you were at school, would you still choose nursing as a career?

Yes	( )	1 422
No	( )	5
Not sure	( )	3

THE END

Thank you very much for your co-operation.

If you have any extra comments to make about the questionnaire, and the problems raised (or not raised) we should appreciate it if you would mention them here. . .

SELECT BIBLIOGRAPHY

Abel, P.M., Farmer, P., Hunter, M. and Shipp, P. 'Nursing Manpower: a Sound Statistical Base for Policy Making', *Nursing Times*, occasional papers 5-8, January 1976

Abel-Smith, B. *A History of the Nursing Profession* (Heinemann, London, 1960)

Alderfer, C. 'An Empirical Test of a Theory of Human Needs', *Organisational Behaviour and Human Performance*, vol.4 (1969), pp.142-75

Austin, R. 'Sex and Gender in the Future of Nursing', *Nursing Times*, occasional papers 1-2, 25 August and 1 September 1977

Barron, R.D. and Norris, G.M. 'Sexual Divisions and the Dual Labour Market' in D. Barker and S. Allen (eds.), *Dependence and Exploitation in Work and Marriage* (Longman, London, 1976)

Bartholomew, D.J. (ed.), *Manpower Planning* (Penguin, Harmondsworth, 1976)

Beechey, V. 'Women and Production: a Critical Analysis of Some Sociological Theories of Women's Work' in A. Kuhn and A. Wolpe (eds.), *Feminism and Materialism* (Routledge and Kegan Paul, London, 1978)

Behrend, H. 'A Note on Labour Turnover and the Individual Factory', *Journal of Industrial Economics*, vol.22 (1953), pp.58-64

——, 'Absence and Labour Turnover in a Changing Economic Climate', *Occupational Psychology*, vol.27 (1955), pp.69-79

Bendix, R. *Work and Authority in Industry* (Harper and Row, New York, 1954)

Beynon, H. *Working for Ford* (Allen Lane, London, 1973)

Blauner, R. *Alienation and Freedom* (Chicago University Press, Chicago, 1964)

Bowey, A.M. 'Labour Stability Curves and a Labour Stability Index', *British Journal of Industrial Relations*, vol.7 (1969), pp.71-83

Braverman, H. *Labour and Monopoly Capital* (Monthly Review Press, New York, 1974)

Briggs, A. (Chairman), *Report of the Committee on Nursing* (HMSO, London, 1972), Cmnd.7115

Brissenden, P., and Frankel, E. *Labour Turnover in Industry: A Statistical Analysis* (Macmillan, New York, 1922)

Brown, R.G.S., and Stones, R.W. *The Male Nurse*, Occasional Papers on Social Administration, no.52 (Bell, London, 1973)

Bryant, D.T. 'A Survey of the Development of Manpower Planning Policies', *British Journal of Industrial Relations*, vol.3 (1965), pp.279-90

Byrt, W.J. 'Methods of Measuring Labour Turnover', *Personnel Practice Bulletin*, vol.13 (1957), pp.6-14

Carpenter, M. 'The New Managerialism and Professionalism in Nursing' in M. Stacey *et al.* (eds.), *Health and the Division of Labour* (Croom Helm, London, 1977)

Cockburn, C. *The Local State* (Pluto Press, London, 1977)

Cousins, J.M. *Values and Value in the Labour Market*, Working Papers in Sociology, no.9 (University of Durham, n.d.)

Daniel, W. 'Industrial Behaviour and the Orientation to Work — a Critique', *Journal of Management Studies*, vol.8 (1971), pp.329-35

Department of Employment. *New Earnings Survey 1975* (HMSO, London, 1975)

——, *Women and Work: A Statistical Survey*, Manpower Paper, no.9 (HMSO, London, 1974)

——, *Women and Work: A Review*, Manpower Paper, no.11 (HMSO, London, 1975)

Department of Health and Social Security. *Leavers: Standard Measures and Classifications*, Maplin Report, no.1 (DHSS, London, 1975)

Dixon, P., and Pace, A. 'Manpower Planning' in E. Raybould (ed.), *A Guide for Nurse Managers* (Blackwell, London, 1977)

Dubin, R. 'Industrial Workers' Worlds: a Study of the "Central Life Interests" of Industrial Workers', *Social Problems*, vol.3 (1956), pp.131-42

Dunkerley, D., and Mercer, G. 'Wastage among Student and Trained Nurses', *Nursing Times*, 30 January 1975

Etzioni, A. (ed.), *The Semi-Professions and the Organisation* (Free Press, New York, 1969)

Fleishman, E.A., and Harris, E.F. 'Patterns of Leadership Behaviour Related to Employee Grievances and Turnover', *Personnel Psychology* vol.15 (1962), pp.43-56

Forbes, A.F. 'Non-Parametric Methods of Estimating the Survivor Function', *The Statistician*, vol.20 (1971), pp.27-52

Gardiner, J. 'Women in the Labour Process and Class Structure' in A. Hunt (ed.), *Class and Class Structure* (Lawrence and Wishart, London, 1977)

Gaudet, F.J. *Labour Turnover: Calculation and Cost*, Research Study, no.39 (American Management Association, New York, 1960)

Gavron, H. *The Captive Wife* (Penguin, Harmondsworth, 1966)

General Council for England and Wales. *Annual Report 1976-77* (GNC, London, 1978)

Goldthorpe, J.H. 'Attitudes and Behaviour of Car Assembly Workers: a Deviant Case and a Theoretical Critique', *British Journal of Sociology*, vol.17 (1966), pp.227-44

——, 'The Social Action Approach to Industrial Sociology – a Reply to Daniel', *Journal of Management Studies*, vol.7 (1970), pp.199-208

——, 'Daniel on Orientation to Work – a Final Comment', *Journal of Management Studies*, vol.9 (1972), pp.266-73

Goldthorpe, J.H., Lockwood, D., Bechhofer, F., and Platt, J. *The Affluent Worker: Industrial Attitudes and Behaviour* (Cambridge University Press, Cambridge, 1972)

Gordon, D.M. *Theories of Poverty and Underemployment* (D.C. Heath, Lexington, 1972)

Gough, I. 'State Expenditure in Advanced Capitalism', *New Left Review*, no.92 (1975), pp.53-92

Greenwood, T.F. 'Problems of Industrial Organisation', *Journal of the Royal Statistical Society*, vol.82 (1919), pp.186-209

Greystoke, J.R., Thomason, G.F., and Murphy, T.J. 'Labour Turnover Surveys', *Personnel Management*, vol.34 (1952), pp.158-65

Habenstein, R., and Christ, E. *Professionaliser, Traditionaliser and Utiliser* (University of Missouri, Columbia, 1955)

Hackett, J.D. *Labor Management* (Macmillan, New York, 1929)

Harris, A. *Labour Mobility in Britain* (HMSO, London, 1963)

Hawkins, K. *Conflict and Change* (Holt, Rinehart and Winston, London, 1972)

Hedberg, M. 'The Turnover of Labour in Industry: an Actuarial Study', *Acta Sociologica*, vol.5 (1961), pp.129-43

——, *The Process of Turnover*, Report no.52 (Swedish Council for Personnel Administration, Stockholm, 1967)

Herbst, P.G. 'Organisational Commitment: a Decision Process Model', *Acta Sociologica*, vol.7 (1963), pp.34-45

Herzberg, F., Mausner, B., and Synderman, B. *The Motivation to Work* (Wiley, New York, 1959)

Hicks, J.R. *The Theory of Wages* (Macmillan, London, 1932)

Hill, J.M. 'A Consideration of Labour Turnover as a Resultant of a Quasi-Stationary Process', *Human Relations*, vol.4 (1951), pp.255-64

——, *The Seafaring Career* (Tavistock Institute, London, 1972)

Hockey, L. *Women in Nursing* (Hodder and Stoughton, London, 1976)

Hughes, E., Hughes, H., and Deutscher, I. *Twenty Thousand Nurses
   Tell Their Story* (Lippincott, Philadelphia, 1958)
Hunt, A. *A Survey of Women's Employment* (Government Social
   Survey, London, 1968)
Hyman, R. 'Economic Motivation and Labour Stability', *British
   Journal of Industrial Relations*, vol.8 (1970), pp.159-78
Ingham, G.K. *Size of Industrial Organisation and Worker Behaviour*
   (Cambridge University Press, Cambridge, 1970)
Jefferys, M. *Mobility in the Labour Market* (Routledge and Kegan Paul,
   London, 1964)
Katz, F. 'Nurses' in A. Etzioni (ed.), *The Semi-Professions and the
   Organisation* (Free Press, Glencoe, 1969), ch.2
Keidan, O., and Jones, C. 'Are Married Nurses Drop-outs?', *Nursing
   Times*, Occasional paper, 21 May 1970
Kerr, C. 'The Balkanisation of Labour Markets' in E.W. Bakke (ed.),
   Labour Mobility and Economic Opportunity (MIT Press, Cambridge,
   1954)
Lane, K.F., and Andrew, J.E. 'A Method of Labour Turnover Analysis',
   Journal of the Royal Statistical Society, Series A, vol.118 (1955),
   pp.296-323
Lawrence, J. 'Manpower and Personnel Models in Britain', *Personnel
   Review*, vol.2 (1973), pp.4-27
Lawton, U. 'Why Nurses Abandon the Profession', *Nursing Times*,
   6 August 1970, pp.1022-3
Levine, E. 'Turnover among Nursing Personnel in General Hospitals',
   Hospitals, 5 September 1957, pp.50-3
Lind, G., Luckman, J., and Wiseman, C. *Qualified Nurses Outwith the
   Scottish N.H.S.* (Tavistock Institute of Human Relations, 1977)
Lockwood, D. *The Blackcoated Worker: a Study in Class Consciousness*
   (Allen and Unwin, London, 1958)
Long, A., and Mercer, G. 'Turnover of Labour in Nursing – Part 2',
   Health Services Manpower Review, no.4 (1977), pp.6-10
Long, A., and Mercer, G. 'Nursing Turnover: an Exploration through
   Path Analysis', unpublished paper, University of Leeds, 1978
Long, J.R. *Labour Turnover under Full Employment*, Studies in
   Economics and Society, Monograph A2 (University of Birmingham,
   1951)
MacGuire, J.M. *Threshold to Nursing*, Occasional Papers on Social
   Administration, no.30 (Bell, London, 1969)
Mackay, D.I. 'Wages and Labour Turnover' in D. Robinson (ed.),
   Local Labour Markets and Wage Structure (Gower Press, London,

1970), pp.68-99

Mackay, D.I., Boddy, D., Brack, J., Diack, J.A., and Jones, N. *Labour Markets* (Allen and Unwin, London, 1971)

Makower, H., Marshak, J., and Robinson, H. 'Studies in the Mobility of Labour: Analysis for Great Britain: Part II', *Oxford Economic Papers,* no.4 (1940), pp.39-62

Mangione, T.W. 'Turnover — Some Psychological and Demographic Correlates' in R. Quinn and T.W. Mangione (eds.), *The 1969-1970 Survey of Working Conditions* (Survey Research Centre, University of Michigan, 1973)

Mann, M. *Workers on the Move* (Cambridge University Press, Cambridge, 1973)

Manson, T. 'Management, the Professions and the Unions' in M. Stacey *et al.* (eds.), *Health and the Division of Labour* (Croom Helm, London, 1977)

March, J.G., and Simon, H.A. *Organisations* (Wiley, New York, 1958)

Maslow, A.H. *Motivation and Personality* (Harper and Row, New York, 1954)

Mayo, E., and Lombard, G. *Teamwork and Labour Turnover in the Aircraft Industry in Southern California*, Business Research Studies, no.32 (Harvard Graduate School of Business Administration, Cambridge, Mass., 1944)

Mercer, G. 'Fluctuations over Time in the Rate of Nursing Turnover', unpublished paper, University of Leeds, 1978

——, and Long, A. 'Turnover of Labour in Nursing — Part 1', *Health Services Manpower Review*, no.3 (1977), pp.8-18

——, and Mould, C. 'An Investigation into the Level and Character of Labour Turnover amongst Trained Nurses', unpublished report for the DHSS, University of Leeds, 1976

——, Mould, C., and Taggart, L. 'Nurses on the Move', *Nursing Times*, 25 March 1976, pp.441-3

——, Taggart, L., and Mould, C. 'Nurses on the Move', *Health and Social Service Journal*, 7 August 1976, pp.1432-3

Meszaros, I. *Marx's Theory of Alienation* (Merlin, London, 1970)

Moores, B. 'Patterns of Student Nurse Wastage', *International Journal of Nursing Studies*, vol.8 (1971), pp.61-71

Moreton, T. 'Towards a Model of Labour Turnover and Job Choice', *Personnel Review*, vol.3 (1974), pp.12-22

Morton-Williams, J., and Berthoud, R. 'Nurses Attitude Survey', unpublished report on Postal Survey, Social and Community Planning Research, London, 1971 — referred to in text as 'Nurse

Interview Survey'

Morton-Williams, J., and Berthoud, R. 'Nurses Attitude Survey', unpublished report on Postal Survey, Social and Community Planning Research, London, 1971 — referred to in text as 'Nurse Postal Survey'

Myers, C. 'Labour Market Theory and Empirical Research' in J. Dunlop (ed.), *The Theory of Wage Determination* (Macmillan, London, 1957)

Myrdal, A., and Klein, V. *Women's Two Roles* (Routledge and Kegan Paul, London, 1970)

Nelson, E. 'The Market Place for Manpower', unpublished report for Southampton and S.W. Hampshire Health District, Southampton, 1977

Northcott, C. *Personnel Management*, 4th edn (Pitman, London, 1968)

Olesen, V., and Whittaker, E. *The Silent Dialogue* (Jossey-Bass, Pennsylvania, 1968)

Orzack, L. 'Work as a "Central Life Interest" of Professionals', *Social Problems*, vol.7 (1959), pp.125-32

Palmer, G. *The Reluctant Job Changer* (University of Pennsylvania Press, Phil., 1962)

Parnes, H.S. *Research on Labour Mobility* (SSRC, New York, 1954)

Pettman, B.O. 'Some Factors Influencing Labour Turnover: a Review of Research Literature', *Industrial Relations Journal*, vol.4 (1973), pp.43-61

——, (ed.), *Labour Turnover and Retention* (Gower Press, London, 1975)

——, 'External and Personal Determinants of Labour Turnover' in B.O. Pettman (ed.), *Labour Turnover and Retention* (Gower Press, London, 1975), ch.2

——, *Womanpower: an Underutilised Resource* (MCB Monographs, Bradford, 1977)

Price, J.L. 'A Theory of Turnover' in B.O. Pettman (ed.), *Labour Turnover and Retention* (Gower Press, London, 1975), ch.3

——, 'The Measurement of Turnover', *Industrial Relations Journal*, vol.6 (1975/6), pp.34-46

——, *The Study of Turnover* (Iowa State University Press, Iowa, 1977)

——, and Bluedorn, A. 'Intent to Leave as a Measure of Turnover', unpublished paper, University of Iowa, 1977

——, and Bluedorn, A. 'Test of a Causal Model of Organisational Turnover', unpublished paper, University of Iowa, 1977

Rapoport, R., and Rapoport, R. *Dual Career Families* (Penguin,

Harmondsworth, 1971)

Redfern, S. 'Absence and Wastage in Trained Nurses: a Selective Review of the Literature', *Journal of Advanced Nursing*, no.3 (1978), pp.231-49

Revans, R.W. *Hospitals: Communication, Choice and Change* (Tavistock, London, 1972)

Reynolds, L.G. *The Structure of Labour Markets* (Harper, New York, 1951)

Rice, A.K. 'The Relative Independence of Sub-institutions as Illustrated by Departmental Labour Trunover', *Human Relations*, vol.5 (1952), pp.83-90

Rice, A.K., Hill, J.M., and Trist, E.L. 'The Representation of Labour Turnover as a Social Process', *Human Relations*, vol.3 (1950), pp.349-72

Rice, A.K., and Trist, E.L. 'Institutional and Sub-institutional Determinants of Change in Labour Turnover', *Human Relations*, vol.5 (1952), pp.347-71

Ride, T. 'Why Have All the Nurses Gone?', *Nursing Times*, 30 May 1974, pp.820-1

Robinson, D. *Wage Drift, Fringe Benefits and Manpower Distribution* (OECD, Paris, 1968)

Ronan, W. 'A Study of and Some Concepts Concerning Labour Turnover', *Occupational Psychology*, vol.41 (1967), pp.193-202

Sadler, J., and Whitworth, T. *Reserves of Nurses* (HMSO, London, 1975)

Saleh, S., and Hyde, J. 'Intrinsic vs. Extrinsic Orientation and Job Satisfaction', *Occupational Psychology*, vol.43 (1969), pp.47-53

Salmon, B. (Chairman), *Report of the Committee on Senior Nursing Staff Structure* (DHSS, London, 1966)

Scottish Home and Health Department, *Nursing Manpower Planning Reports*, nos.1 to 4 (SHHD, Edinburgh, 1974-5)

Seear, B.N. *Re-entry of Women to the Labour Market after an Interruption in Employment* (OECD, Paris, 1971)

Silcock, H. 'The Phenomenon of Labour Turnover', *Journal of the Royal Statistical Society*, Series A, vol.117 (1954), pp.429-40

Silverman, D. *The Theory of Organisations* (Heinemann, London, 1970)

Sims, A., Long, P., and Saunders, M. 'The Trained Nurse in England and Wales', unpublished report, General Nursing Council, London, 1977

Sonquist, J. *Multivariate Model Building* (University of Michigan, Ann Arbor, 1970)

Stainer, G. *Manpower Planning* (Heinemann, London, 1971)

Stoikov, V., and Raimon, R.L. 'Determinants of the Differences in the Quit Rate Among Industries', *American Economic Review*, vol.58 (1968), pp.1283-98

Tainto, R. *Determinants of Labour Turnover in a Firm* (Helsinki School of Economics, Helsinki, 1977)

Thomas, C. 'The Mobility of Labour in Great Britain', *Occupational Psychology*, vol.27 (1953), pp.215-20

Van der Merwe, R., and Miller, S. 'The Measurement of Labour Turnover: a Critical Appraisal and a Suggested New Approach', *Human Relations*, vol.24, pp.233-53

——, 'The Measurement of Labour Turnover' in B.O. Pettman (ed.), *Labour Turnover and Retention* (Gower Press, London, 1975), ch.1

Vroom, V. *Work and Motivation* (Wiley, New York, 1964)

Wedderburn, D., and Crompton, R. *Workers' Attitudes and Technology* (Cambridge University Press, Cambridge, 1972)

Weir, M. (ed.), *Job Satisfaction* (Fontana, Glasgow, 1976)

White, C., and MacGuire, M.C. 'Job Satisfaction and Dissatisfaction amongst Hospital Nursing Supervisors', *Nursing Research*, no.22 (1973), pp.25-30

Wieland, G. 'Studying and Measuring Turnover', *International Journal of Nursing Studies*, vol.6 (1969), pp.61-9

Williams, W.M. (ed.), *Occupational Choice* (Allen and Unwin, London, 1974)

INDEX

absenteeism 17, 12
accession rate 67-72
accommodation, as predictor of
    turnover 94, 109, 120-1
age: completed length of service
    61-2; crude turnover rate 67;
    direction of turnover 82; pre-
    dictor of turnover 94, 106,
    111-21, 125, 155
agency nursing 60, 80-4 *passim*,
    see also non-NHS nursing
average length of service *see* com-
    pleted length of service

Barron, R.D. and Norris, G.M.
    13-14
Beechey, V. 14
Behrend, H. 96
Blauner, R. 134
break from work 10, 83-4, 99-100,
    108-10
Briggs Committee Report: nurse
    participation rate 60-2, 82;
    nursing labour market 12, 17;
    nursing turnover 8, 52, 156
Brissenden, P. and Frankel, E.
    7, 21, 30, 32

career satisfaction, as predictor of
    turnover 104, 111-21 *passim*,
    123
charge nurse 42, 49, 58, 71, 81, *see
    also* grade, male nurses, ward sister
child(ren): as predictor of turnover
    94, 107, 111-21 *passim*, 125, 155
cohort turnover rate: definition
    33-5; variation 72-5, 152,
    see also grade, hospital, hours
    worked, sex of nurse
communication among nurses, as
    predictor of turnover 108, 111-21
    passim, 125-6
community ties, as predictor of
    turnover 100, 107-8, 110
controllable/uncontrollable turn-
    over 20, 24-5
corporate management 9, 11-14.
    16, *see also* nursing administration

corrected separation rate 32, 65-9
costs of turnover 8, 12, 25, 156
crèche facilities 16, 26
crude turnover rate: definition 30-3,
    35; variation 63-72, *see also*
    accession rate, corrected separation
    rate, separation rate

demand for nurses 8, 10
Department of Health and Social
    Security (DHSS) 7, 15, 32
desirability of movement 101-6, 155
direction of turnover 24, 78-9,
    118-21, 156-7
District General Hospital (DGH)
    22, 42-3, 54
domestic factors in turnover
    125-8, 147-51, 157
Dubin, R. 135

ease of movement 101,103,106-9,155
economic conditions and turnover
    10-11, 17, 25, 57, 71. 96-7
educational attainment, as predictor
    of turnover 100, 105, 111-21 *passim*
enrolled nurse (SEN/SSEN): cohort
    turnover rate 73-5; completed length
    of service 49-63 *passim*; crude turn-
    over rate 64-71; force of separation
    76-8; internal transfer 56-9; job
    satisfaction 140-6; position in
    nursing 16, 157-8; previous work
    record 58; sample 42; self-perception
    of mobility 149, *see also* grade

female nurses: cohort turnover rate
    75; completed length of service
    49-63 *passim*; crude turnover rate
    64-71; force of separation 78,
    see also sex of nurse
force of separation: definition 35,
    38-9, 41; variation 75-9
full-time nurses: cohort turnover
    rate 73-5; completed length of
    service 49-63 *passim*; crude turn-
    over rate 64-71; direction of turn-
    over 81-3; force of separation 76-8;
    sample 42, *see also* hours worked

182